SWIMMING POOL WATER

TREATMENT AND QUALITY STANDARDS

POOL WATER TREATMENT ADVISORY GROUP

SWIMMING POOL WATER
TREATMENT AND QUALITY STANDARDS

Produced by the independent Pool Water Treatment Advisory Group, with the support of its member organisations - Sport England, Department for Education & Employment, Ministry of Defence, Amateur Swimming Association, British Association for Chemical Specialities, British Water, Chartered Institute of Environmental Health, Institute of Sport & Recreation Management, Institute of Engineers of Ireland, Institute of Leisure & Amenity Management and the Swimming Pool & Allied Trades Association; also its technical advisers from the Department of the Environment Transport & the Regions, Department of Health, Public Health Laboratory Service and Chartered Institution of Building Services Engineers.

PWTAG would also like to acknowledge the support of the Health & Safety Executive.

Design/production BCPublications
Printed by Micropress Printers Ltd

A chairman's introduction

Four years on from the publication of the best-selling *Pool Water Guide*, it is tempting to say that the present book 'needs no introduction.' But developments over the last five years, and the increased scope of this book, do suggest that some context would be useful.

The principles behind the guidelines in *Pool Water Guide* have not been seriously challenged over the years. But there is one apparently controversial area. Our advocacy of aiming to operate pools with free chlorine residuals under 1mg/l has raised a few hackles. Some people are concerned that such a figure can cause microbiological problems. And they are right. Our targets, in this area and in others, are tailored for a well designed pool, operating well and within its designed bathing load. If these things do not apply, then the free chlorine residual may well have to be higher. And a minimum residual, to cope with an influx of bathers, is necessary. This is spelled out more clearly this time, mainly in chapter 6.

But we are anxious that this should not be a licence for sloppy practices; rather, it should be an encouragement for designers and operators to produce pools that provide bathers with as comfortable a swim as possible. If this requires a higher standard of pre-swim hygiene than is the norm in the UK, so be it. Other European countries can happily enforce a system where a thorough shower before a swim is the norm, and there's no reason why that shouldn't work here as well. It's certainly something PWTAG would like to see.

This book is twice the size of *Pool Water Guide*. So although, like all authors, we might wish that people read it from beginning to end, inevitably users will dip in and out to find the bits they want. To make this as easy as possible, the Contents, the cross-referencing and the Index are very explicit. And if the text reads well, as I believe it does, that is once again thanks largely to the editorial efforts of PWTAG's secretary, Brian Guthrie.

Finally, I would like to thank the authors. All the people and organisations who make up PWTAG's membership (listed on page 136) have contributed. (And many other people commented most usefully on drafts.) But the major burden has been shouldered - over two years, many meetings and much drafting and re-drafting - by an authors' group of PWTAG working under my chairmanship. In thanking these people, I would also thank their employers, who have generously facilitated their efforts. So I thank Tom Devin of FaulknerBrowns Engineering Services - now FES Water Technology Consultants, Howard Gosling of Certikin International, Ralph Riley of the Institute of Sport & Recreation Management, and Dave Whittingham of Thermelek Engineering Services. I would also like to thank my employers, Prominent Fluid Controls.

Andy Elphick

Preface

Pool Water Guide, first published in 1995, replaced *The treatment and quality of swimming pool water*, which was the direct descendant of the 'blue book' - *The Purification of the Water of Swimming Baths*, first published by the Ministry of Health in 1929. *Pool Water Guide* was the product of over a decade's work by the Pool Water Treatment Advisory Group, an independent, self-financed collection of professional, governmental and industry representatives - which took over when the government withdrew from the field. The first edition of *Pool Water Guide* was without doubt the group's most significant single piece of work. It sold out - 4,000 copies.

Swimming Pool Water is twice the size of that book, with updated, often extra information throughout. There is, in particular, new material on source waters, choosing disinfectants, dosing, circulation, delivery, storage, maintenance, cleaning, and protection. There is also detailed information on the makeup of all safety-approved pool chemicals.

But the four years since *Pool Water Guide* was first published have also allowed PWTAG to review and update the information contained in it. So the rest of this volume, although by and large organised like the original, contains significant new information. The PWTAG research work at Cranfield University (under the auspices of the Pool Water Research Foundation - see page 136) has informed the preparation of this book.

But the philosophy behind it is unchanged and deserves restating.

We are concerned that our books, and indeed the work of PWTAG, have not been brought within the regulatory framework of an appropriate government department. Although PWTAG's work is recognised by all major interests in health and safety, sport, education, national and local government, we continue to campaign for standards on pool water quality.

It is done for drinking water and even coastal waters. Regulations might ensure that every pool used by the public is operated to a prescribed standard, with competent, qualified staff. This should be the right of every pool user, particularly considering the harm an unskilled operator can cause. Mandatory standards are not remotely imminent - although PWTAG and the British Standards Institution are discussing a voluntary BS. The World Health Organisation, also, has enlisted PWTAG to help in its preparation of guidelines on swimming pools.

Meanwhile the demand for guidance is insistent. It is clear from problems with swimming pools that managers and operators need inspiration, advice and guidance now. So, perhaps paradoxically, PWTAG has advocated a shift away from prescription. Certainly *Pool Water Guide* reinforced the principles of the 'blue book', adjusted and updated as appropriate in the light of today's technology, products and our continuing experience. But the significant change we have introduced is not a new process, chemical or item of equipment. It is a change of emphasis, away from prescriptive standards and methods towards reasoning, understanding and a measured response.

This change will not suit everybody. A prescriptive approach seems simpler to understand and implement, appears easier to monitor. But it does not guarantee good quality water. This book encourages pool operators to minimise the use of chemicals - both the number and range used and the quantities of, for example, disinfectant. The purpose of this approach is, in particular, to minimise their impact on the water and air in pool buildings and on the fabric of the building itself. It seeks to create greater understanding that in pool water treatment every change has an effect. Design, management, source water, chemicals, bathers, filtration, hydraulics, operation, control: all are inter-related in a complex way which pool

operators need to understand. That is why this book has much new material on design, and continually relates this to subsequent operation of the pool.

This book should be used by designers, suppliers, operators and managers of any non-domestic pool - from a large municipal leisure complex to a small hotel pool. The book has been compiled with a 'conventional' pool in mind - rectangular, indoor, no extras, used by all ages. But the principles certainly hold for all types of pool, and many parts of the book (including Chapters 2 and 3) spell out how the practice varies with the different types of pool.

This book does not focus on costs, although there is, in Chapter 5, a section which outlines the relatively small part that chemical treatment makes up of the cost of a pool. Nevertheless, the guidance we provide, if ignored, does carry very serious cost penalties. It is important that all who operate or plan to set up swimming pools are aware of the essential requirements. Ensuring the health and comfort of all pool users starts with planning, design and construction and goes on to management, operation, training and a

continual drive for improved quality. Failure to meet these fundamantal requirements undermines the welfare of both users and the pool itself, and ultimately the whole operation.

As a nation we are increasingly aware of health and the needs of individuals and society. We are also continually seeking better quality, particularly in our leisure time. Swimming is one of the most popular forms of physical activity. Demand is predicted to increase, but standards must rise to meet rising expectations. A healthy, quality swimming pool experience brings enjoyment and satisfaction to the user. Let this, rather than cost, underly the future operation of pools.

A code of practice? In the absence of laws, regulations or mandatory standards on pool management, operators and others might look towards a code of practice. This book contains the raw materials for such a code. If its principles are absorbed - and the various guideline values for loading, circulation, pollution control, disinfection, monitoring, filtration, etc followed - then those responsible for pools will be in a position to draw up a code of practice.

Contents

An architect's drawing for a 25m pool

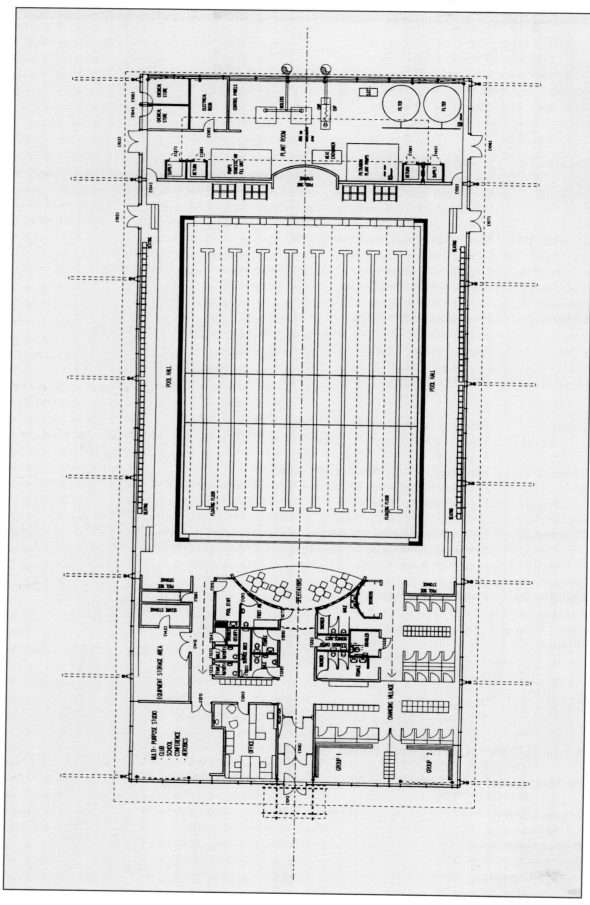

Chapter 1

Pool water treatment

Swimming pools generally get their basic resource supplied by a water company - mains water that has been treated to make it fit to drink. Yet in a pool without any further treatment, mains water would often be unsuitable for swimming - if only because of its turbidity. To understand why this is, and what pool designers and operators should know about their water supply, this chapter describes how mains water is derived and treated - by water companies and by pool operators. It also deals with the important subject of pool water dilution. There is a section on discharge of pool water.

WATER STANDARDS

The English and Welsh water consumer is protected by water quality standards in the Water Supply (Water Quality) Regulations 1989, in line with EC directives. (Different but similar regulations apply in Scotland and Northern Ireland.) World Health Organisation (WHO) drinking water guidelines give a global view. There are no equivalent standards for pool water (though consumers increasingly aware of drinking water standards may well come to expect them), so drinking water standards are used as guidelines where appropriate.

The Table compares drinking water standards with those for pools. There are some parameters that would suggest immediate treatment for pool water use, even when their concentration is well within drinking water standards. For example, although most water supplies have a turbidity of less than 1 nephelometric turbidity unit (NTU), those with a turbidity of up to 4NTU would need to be reduced by a factor of about 10. In other respects it should be chemically satisfactory - and, of course, healthy.

Mains and swimming pool water compared

	Water supply standard values	Swimming pool recommended values
Turbidity	4 formazin turbidity units (FTU) max	0.5 nephelometric turbidity units (NTU - equivalent to FTU)
Temperature	25°C max	27-30°C
pH value	9.5 max 5.5 min	7.8 max 7.2 min
Sulphate	250mg SO_4/litre max	360mg SO_4/litre max
Sodium	150mgNa/litre max (3 yearly average)	No recommendation
Magnesium	50mgMg/litre	No recommendation
Calcium	250mgCa/litre (annual average)	75-150mg$CaCO_3$/litre (18-36mgCa/litre) - a range; see page 79
Total hardness	60mgCa/litre min (only for water softened at the treatment works)	75mg$CaCO_3$/litre min (30mgCa/litre)
Alkalinity	30mgHCO_3/litre min (at treatment works)	75- 200mg$CaCO_3$/litre
Chloride	400mgCl/litre max (annual average)	No recommendation
Conductivity/Total dissolved solids	1,500µS/cm at 20°C max	3,000mg/l max (c 4,250µS/cm)
Trihalomethanes (THMs)	100µg/litre max (3-monthly average for sum of 4 THMs)	100µg/litre max

RAW WATER SOURCES

Water for drinking is taken from deep boreholes, shallow wells, springs, lowland lakes, reservoirs or rivers, as well as upland reservoirs and streams. The nature of the rock or soil in contact with the water as it passes from rainfall to tap will determine the dissolved or entrained minerals etc in it.

Water will dissolve little from hard rocks such as granite, in terms of hardness, alkalinity or mineral salts. This produces the soft waters found in many parts of Wales, Scotland and northern England. The limestone or chalk aquifers and lowland rivers of the rest of Britain tend to provide the elements of hard water (calcium salts). Mains water is increasingly transported over long distances; and a region may receive soft water from a distant upland source and hard water from a local underground or impounded source. Further, in order to satisfy demand and maintain flexibility, it is quite normal in some areas to supply sometimes hard water, sometimes soft, sometimes a blend of the two.

MAINS WATER TREATMENT

Treatment of raw water sources varies a lot depending on the nature of the raw water. Some requires a lot of treatment, some relatively little. It may involve sedimentation (to remove solids), coagulation (to remove colour and facilitate the removal of solids), filtration and disinfection. Chlorine - as gas or liquid sodium hypochlorite - is almost universally used, to ensure microbiological protection right up to the tap. Other disinfectants are less often used - ozone (to help destroy certain microorganisms and oxidise some organic substances including pesticides), chlorine dioxide (if the water would produce undesirable byproducts with chlorine) and ultraviolet radiation (for small underground sources, and to remove organics). Rivers may carry industrial, agricultural and sewage works pollution: the appropriate treatments will deal with these.

Some water works add ammonia as well as chlorine to produce a monochloramine residual in the supply; this gives a longer-lasting disinfectant active against biofilm formation inside pipes, etc. Monochloramine can be present at 0.2-0.5mg/l in the supply. Disinfectants based on bromine and chlorinated isocyanurates are rarely used for drinking water.

KNOWING THE WATER

Given the variations in water supply, it is vital that pool designers determine what the quality of water supplied will be, including its likely variation. This should influence the choice of water treatment (see page 28). All water suppliers are required by regulations to maintain a public record of the quality of water supplied to each water supply zone. This includes the results of analyses. Users are entitled to inspect the record and have a free copy of it for their water supply. This will provide designers with data on the past quality. They should, however, also ask water suppliers for details of likely changes in the future. The Table on page 9 gives the relevant parameters.

TREATING WATER FOR POOL USE

The water companies' treatment processes provide a safe water, but - especially if from river or reservoir (surface waters) - likely to contain some or all of:
- organic materials, including humic acid - a precursor of the undesirable chlorination byproducts, trihalomethanes, which themselves may be present
- lime and other alkalis added to prevent corrosion in the supply network
- phosphates (which encourage algae in a

Typical potable water treatment

FLOCCULATION → FILTRATION → SOFTENING

Polymer, Alum

Lime

Ammonia (pre-or post)

FLUORIDATION ← pH ADJUST/ CORROSION INHIBITION ← CHLORINATION

Hydrofluosilicic acid   pH   Caustic Phosphate Cl_2 Sodium hypochlorite

Sodium hypochlorite

Cl_2

WATER DISTRIBUTION SYSTEM

RECHLORINATION

pool) added to prevent lead dissolving from pipework

- substances at levels which, if boosted by any aspect of the pool water treatment, may take levels over the pool guideline limits.

This makes careful control of the pool's disinfection, pH, alkalinity and coagulation essential. And if the mains water has a chloramine residual, this may require a slightly higher level of chlorination.

In general, the importance of a balance between public health demands and consumer acceptability are similar for both drinking and swimming waters. Disinfection cannot be compromised, but it is well worth aiming to minimise both disinfectant levels and the formation of unwanted substances including disinfection byproducts. Dilution (see below) is an important factor in this.

DISINFECTION

Strictly, disinfection means removing the risk of infection, but in the context of swimming pools the term acknowledges that their water cannot be sterile. A few living, but normally harmless microorganisms will always be present; disinfection aims to keep their number to a minimum and to ensure that any harmful organisms entering the pool water are rapidly inactivated so that the water will not transmit infection to bathers. (See Chapter 14.) Proper disinfection is achieved primarily by maintaining the correct concentration of disinfectant in the water, although filtration is also important.

At the same time other water quality parameters, in particular pH value, must be kept at the correct values for disinfectant to act effectively and efficiently (see Chapter 13).

For disinfection to proceed freely the water should be clear and free of suspended material which may shelter the microorganisms from disinfectant activity. Equally, the disinfectant must be given time to kill the microbes. Each species of microbe is different and its destruction will require a particular level of disinfectant and amount of time. In general the degree of disinfection (exposure or CT value) is directly proportional to exposure to the disinfectant.

For example: Exposure value = Contact time x Free chlorine residual (at the end of the time). If contact time is expressed in minutes and chlorine in mg/l, the unit of exposure value is mgmin/l.

The WHO guidelines for drinking water quality recommend 30min exposure to 0.5mg/l chlorine at a maximum pH of 8 - gives a CT value) of 15mgmin/l. This seems high compared to the residual levels advocated for public swimming pools. But the continuous treatment in a recirculating pool allows for extended contact time. On the other hand, a pH of 7.2 rather than 8 increases the CT value roughly threefold; and the higher temperature of pool water compared to drinking water increases the disinfection reaction of chlorine with bacteria roughly fourfold. So pool water disinfection should proceed rapidly enough in a well-run pool.

Many disinfectants are also capable of oxidising waste matter, controlling the build-up of what is the food for many microorganisms (as well as a water contaminant in its own right). Mains water contains a certain amount of such material, but the chief sources are sweat, skin particles, mucus and urine. Such bather pollution can and should be minimised by pre-swim hygiene (see page 28)

Disinfection must extend beyond the pool water to the filters (see Chapter 12): in the filter plant, microorganisms often find excellent conditions for rapid reproduction - warmth, darkness, a bed (of sand usually) to lie on and a plentiful supply of food. Without adequate disinfection, filter beds may harbour pathogenic organisms including some amoebae, *Staphylococcus aureus* and *Pseudomonas aeruginosa*.

DILUTION WITH FRESH WATER

Disinfection and filtration will not remove all pollutants. So the design of a swimming pool should recognise the need to dilute the pool water with fresh water. Dilution limits the buildup of pollutants from bathers and elsewhere, the byproducts of disinfection, and various other dissolved chemicals.

To some extent, dilution is effected through the replacement of water used in backwashing.

But backwashing is often not frequent enough (it should be at least weekly) to keep the concentration of unwanted pollutants at an acceptably low level. And some pollutants can be reduced only by dilution. If dilution is inadequate, bather discomfort can result. So pool operators should be prepared to replace pool water as a regular part of their water treatment regime, at a rate of 30 litres per bather per day. If this can be done gradually, in response to bather entry, all the better. The inlets, outlets and pipework should be planned accordingly. As well as making bathing (and the pool hall atmosphere generally) more comfortable, proper dilution can help protect the fabric of the building by reducing the level of contaminants in the air above the pool.

Although 30 litres per bather per day might seem an intimidating amount of water, operators are likely to be diluting already to as much as 50% of that level just by backwashing. Fresh water should, ideally, be metered to allow accurate measurement and monitoring of dilution rates; and added gradually throughout opening hours, linked to bather throughput. Diluting up to 30 litres per bather per day clearly has practical implications in terms of how water is removed and the fresh water added, heated etc. But if it leads pool managers to undertake a comprehensive audit of water, energy and effluent costs, then that is another real benefit. Managers should at the same time evaluate the dilution that can be introduced by pre-swim showering with pool water (see page 29). And the relevant water authorities must be consulted about discharges of water from backwashing/dilution.

DISCHARGE

Since 1994, backwash water has been classified as a trade effluent. In England and Wales discharge to sewers requires the consent of the local water service company; discharge to a water course must be authorised by the regional office of the Environment Agency. In Scotland the relevant authorities are the local water authority and Environment Protection Agency respectively; in N Ireland, the Department of the Environment.

These authorities may have specific requirements about the rate and quality of discharges from backwashing, dilution, pool emptying, etc. It is important in any case for pool managers to consult the authorities about their operation and any changes to it. Backwash water may need dechlorination (see page 83) if it is going to a surface water drain.

Chapter 2

Types of pool

This book has been compiled with one type of pool particularly in mind - the so-called 'conventional' pool. That would be a rectangular, indoor pool, used by people of all ages and with no extra water features - the sort of pool sometimes called 'main', 'public', 'municipal', even 'competition'. (This chapter returns to the conventional, or typical pool on page 18 - and it is the model used throughout the book.) In fact, the recommendations in this book do hold in principle for all non-domestic pools, but may need to be varied to apply to the many kinds of 'non-conventional' pools.

These variations are recognised throughout this - for example, and crucially, in the section on designing turnover periods, etc for leisure and other pools (page 20). Page 116 gives the recommended temperatures for the different types of pool. But there are other considerations - not least in deciding what sort of pool is required.

WHAT POOL?

Faced with the possibility of providing a new pool, those responsible need to evaluate the requirements and decide what type of pool will satisfy them. This judgement should be made as a preliminary to any formal feasibility study that might be necessary. Without it, the pool may be over-specified - and money wasted; or under-specified - and never provide good bathing conditions.

Who is the pool for?
Establishing what customers are being targeted is an important early step. For example, are they:
- the general public in a well-populated urban area
- primary school children in small teaching groups during school time - nothing else
- guests at an hotel (low numbers, probably)
- health club members doing fitness swimming
- medical patients having therapy in the pool

- competitive swimmers training
- swimmers of all types, but from a small, isolated community
- clients of an outdoor camping park - quiet mostly, but with very busy periods
- leisure bathers attracted as part of a wider tourism initiative - theme park, holiday village, etc?

What programme?
The next stage is to establish how the pool will be used:
- the daily operating period
- the use at different times of the day
- the anticipated bathing load for each type of use
- any special requirements - eg temperature, lanes, play equipment
- the weekly, monthly and annual operating programme.

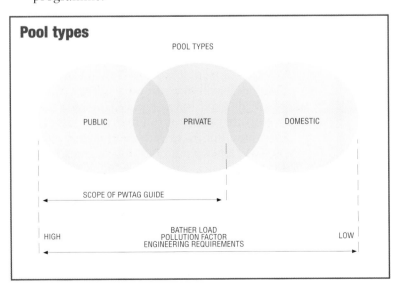

Pool types

POOL TYPES

PUBLIC   PRIVATE   DOMESTIC

SCOPE OF PWTAG GUIDE

HIGH   BATHER LOAD   LOW
POLLUTION FACTOR
ENGINEERING REQUIREMENTS

An example ...

Take the primary school pool mentioned above. A typical design might be a rectangular pool 13x7m with broad steps along one length into water 600mm deep extending to 800mm. The pool could have deck-level circulation - no intimidating freeboard and good contact between teachers and pupils. Tank bottom, low-velocity inlets prevent the agitation or currents that might unbalance a child.

Although a water temperature of 30°C is needed, a pool cover, a well insulated construction, simple background heating and natural rather than mechanical ventilation could be an economical mix.

Because the pool is to be used only by controlled, small groups of children during school time, bathing loads will be steady and predictable. So the engineering can be specified at a lower pitch than a more demanding pool. A turnover of, say, four hours could mean just one filter, with simple backwashing. Disinfection and chemical control should be automatic, but with a simple dosing system and no bulk storage of chemicals. Altogether, the pool should be easy to operate by a school caretaker - but with safety a key issue.

... of change of use

The danger of incorrectly assessing the pool's future use is easily illustrated. The school decides to allow unprogrammed use of the pool by parent teacher groups in the evening and weekend, and community use in the school holidays. The water treatment plant is overstretched, the pool smells, some bathers complain of sore eyes, coughing and wheezing, bacteria counts start to mount...

The alternative is to make provision for a possible expansion of use in the first place. Designing for increased bathing loads, although it will increase the capital cost of the treatment plant (quite possibly a low proportion of the overall build cost - see page 34) would not necessarily increase running costs. A larger plant does not necessarily use more chemicals, nor increase the amount of water needed for backwash - and barely increases overall power requirements if half-duty or variable-speed pumps are installed. And its flexibility may well contribute to a better swimming environment.

The operator's responsibility to plan for safety

- dealt with in more detail on page 119 of this book - starts with defining the purpose for a planned pool.

DEFINITIONS AND TYPES

This section spells out the terms used to describe pool types and what special considerations need to be made to get the water treatment right. It is also an alphabetical guide to the sometimes confusing nomenclature used when defining pools. Even so, terms can be understood differently by different practitioners, and definitions can shift. Words in *italics* refer to other entries in this section. The terms can be combined to define the pool. For example, a basic distinction is between *deck-level* and *freeboard* systems. Yet the two may well be combined in a leisure pool. And a competition pool could be either freeboard or - probably better - deck-level.

Adjustable/Flexible

These terms relate to a moveable floor and/or bulkhead (boom) in the pool tank. The moveable floor gives variable depth. It is important that the turnover period should cope with the biggest bathing load the pool will have, in the area where use is most likely to be concentrated - shallow places, probably (see page 21). Laterally moving bulkheads divide pools into two, usually in any proportion. Perforated panels allow water flow between sections of the pool.

Bubble

Such a pool has bubbles of air introduced via the seat or the floor. Its seating may be arranged like that of a *spa* pool, but is likely to have many more users and a temperature typically 28-32°C.

Community

These are pools designed to meet the needs of a particular, local community. They can be any size; best provided and managed as *dual-use*. The pool water treatment system should meet the guidelines in this book.

Competition

Pools for competition are 25 or 50m long. Where used for ASA (Amateur Swimming Association) championships they should ideally have at least eight lanes, each at least 2m wide. Dimensions for full championship and Olympic pools are given in regulations from FINA (Federation Internationale de Natation Amateur, the world governing body for competitive swimming).

Deck-level
Such pools have the pool water level with the pool surround - removing the most polluted surface water over the edge of the pool into a transfer channel and on to a balance tank. See page 64 for the advantages of this type of pool circulation.

Diving
For steep-entry dives from springboards and fixed platforms, a specially designed pool is needed. The depth and area of water for a diving pool (or pit) is determined by ASA or FINA regulations. A 1m springboard requires a minimum of 3.4m depth; a 10m platform, 5m depth.

If the diving pool is fitted with a moveable floor, to allow a variety of uses, special care must be paid to water circulation hydraulics, as for any *adjustable* arrangement.

Dual-use
These are pools used, at different times, by two or more different types of customer. The term is usually applied to a *school* pool that is also opened to the public for some sessions. If a new pool is planned for dual use, the design (circulation, filtration, disinfection etc) should allow for the probably more demanding public use. If an existing school pool is to be opened to the public, care should be taken to ascertain its design bathing load and not exceed it. In either case, serious consideration should be given to the training and qualifications of those responsible for the operation and management.

Flexible
See *Adjustable*.

Freeboard
A pool whose surround is higher than the water level (ie not a deck-level pool) is freeboard; the term is also used for the distance between the two heights.

Hydrotherapy
These are small pools, usually in hospitals, designed for physiotherapy. They are therefore used by vulnerable people (possibly with wounds, occasionally incontinent), operate at temperatures of over 37°C (up to ten degrees higher than public pools) and are often used (especially by staff) for long periods. As a result, they can be demanding to manage - and the penalties for basic mistakes immediate and dramatic. The principles of water treatment are the same as for conventional pools, and the turnover period (see page 21) should be 1 hour - or even 30min if pollution is likely to be heavy. Equipment, including wheelchairs, must be cleaned thoroughly. The Bibliography has details of the PHLS book, *Hygiene for Hydrotherapy Pools*.

Lazy river
See *Rapids*.

Learner/Teaching/Training
A shallow pool, typically 13m long (or perhaps 16.6m for training), 7m wide with steps along one length; a maximum depth of 0.9m; two 2m training lanes. Because this gives a relatively large surface area to volume ratio, pollution is likely to be high when they are used by young children, so bathing load control is particularly important. Turnover periods (see page 20) should be 30-90 minutes.

Particular attention must be paid to design where a learner pool is to share filtration plant with other pools: in this case, disinfectant dosing, monitoring, controls and heating will usually be separate (but see page 69).

Leisure
There are almost as many different forms of leisure pool as there are leisure pools. And some conventional pools get 'leisurised'. But they tend to have in common an irregular shape and more shallow areas than a conventional pool. This makes for less predictable hydraulics and disinfectant dynamics. So circulation patterns, and inlet and outlet siting, should be carefully designed. The calculations of bathing loads and turnover periods are critical (see page 20). In general, turnover periods will have to be under 90 minutes.

The variable slopes and depths involved, and a tendency to high localised concentrations of bathers, can also result in pollution problems. So localised reductions in turnover period may help, where water volumes are low in relation to bather load.

Water and air features will tend to affect the

dynamics of water treatment. For example, they can expel carbon dioxide from the water, elevating pH values - particularly with soft water. Disinfection and water distribution systems should be as sophisticated in terms of automatic dosing and monitoring as the pools are in terms of features and variations in conditions.

Management will have to watch for eye and nose irritation - in staff as well as swimmers - caused by disinfection byproducts liberated through the combination of relatively high ambient temperatures and humidity and condensation from water features, wave machines etc. The answer to such problems is likely to be proper bathing load control, an appropriate water treatment system, avoiding excessive temperatures, good management of disinfectant residuals and pH, and a decent ventilation system (see Chapter 19).

Access to the pool area from outside, and varied use of the pool, can introduce novel forms of pollution. These issues must be addressed. Even more than with other pools, it is important to have a realistic regime of pre-swim hygiene - good showers and toilets, well signposted and with encouragement to use them (see page 28).

Outdoor

Outdoor pools' special problems arise from the weather - summer and winter; and the

influx of pollution of all sorts - grass, mud, sun tan oils, etc. Sudden sunshine may bring a huge increase in bathers, and a degradation of the chlorine disinfectant by ultraviolet light. Chlorine can be stabilised by adding cyanuric acid (see page 42). The often large volumes of water in outdoor pools should help the pool cope with increases in bathing load, but if the turnover of the large volume is slow, it may be difficult to maintain the appropriate disinfectant residual throughout the pool. In any case, the free chlorine levels should not be less than 1mg/l, and may need to be higher.

The answer to all this is a good testing and dosing regime that is sensitive to fluctuating demands. It may even be necessary to be prepared to dose manually from time to time, but not with bathers in, and not without taking into account health and safety considerations.

In winter, assuming the pool is not used, the water level should be lowered by about 300mm so water does not enter the overflow system. Buoyant objects on the water will absorb ice pressure; and ice should be broken while it it still thin. Occasional disinfection will keep the pool clear of algae and bacteria; there are specific 'winterising' chemicals; a winter cover helps with this, and will also keep out leaves and debris.

Whenever an outdoor pool is covered, the danger of illicit access and drowning must be taken into account. If there is a risk of such access, the cover should be able to bear a person's weight without trapping them.

Paddling

Paddling pools (usually under 0.6m deep) are likely to need the same sort of attention described above for outdoor pools. They may be highly polluted relative to their volume, because children will tend to urinate in them, and introduce pollution from around the pool. So the guidelines on turnover etc in Chapter 3 should be followed closely.

Disinfectant residuals etc should be maintained as for conventional pools, although filtration can be relaxed a little as clarity is not so critical in a uniformly very shallow pool. This may be more difficult if the pool is outdoors, in which case the water should be changed regularly, daily if practicable (but depending on filtration efficiency and build-up of combined chlorine and total dissolved solids). On the other hand, replacing the water lost to evaporation and general use will help. If for any reason circumstances make proper hygiene standards impossible to maintain, paddling pool managers should consider closing the pool altogether.

In any case, dogs must be strictly excluded from paddling pools and their surrounds (as they should from any water-based leisure activity).

Plunge

These pools are used in association with a health suite, to cool bathers by immersion in unheated water (but not less than 10°C). They may be big enough for just one person, or large enough to swim in. The water should be disinfected, filtered, etc like a conventional pool - though, depending on their size, continuous dilution with fresh water may be adequate. Good surface water draw-off, regular water replacement and regular emptying and cleaning are, in any case, key considerations, as body fats can accumulate in them.

Rapids/Lazy river

Also called moving water: pumps and jets under the water surface create a moving channel of water - sometimes down a slope (rapid river ride). Because the water flow is substantial, water distribution does not tend to be a problem. Nevertheless, the distribution system should be able to deal with the full body of water under static conditions - as it will need to do, in any case, when the feature is not operating.

Runouts

These are long horizontal troughs at the end of flumes; they slow down and stop the bather.

Salt water

Treatment of saline pools should be the same as for fresh water pools, except that the materials of filters, pipework, pumps etc - as well as ladders and other poolside equipment - must be resistant to salt water corrosion.

School

School pools that are only ever used by pupils in controlled swimming sessions may be managed quite successfully by adequately trained non-specialist staff using simple disinfection and filtration systems. But if they are used by the public, or if there is a real possibility that this will happen in the future, then the guidance above for dual-use pools should be followed.

In any case it is better, if practicable, to follow the guidelines given in this book for conventional pools. And there is a useful Department for Education & Employment booklet for school pool operators and managers (see Bibliography). Some local education authorities have found that setting up a technical advisory unit for school pools works well.

Spas

Spa pools are of many types, but have in common that they are for sitting in (usually by up to about eight users), rather than swimming, and contain water usually between 32 and 40°C which is filtered and chemically treated. (A pool with untreated water that is replaced after each user, and water agitation of some sort, is a whirlpool bath - sometimes incorrectly called a whirlpool spa.)

Bathing loads may be high in spas; combined with the high temperatures, this can make it difficult to maintain satisfactory disinfectant residuals, pH values and microbiological quality. In general, good water quality can be maintained by control of bathing loads and intervals between sessions (both of which can be specified in the design), turnover periods of

The typical pool

Throughout this book, in order to explain different aspects of operation and design, this typical pool is used as a model. Chapter by chapter, its basic structure is added to as hydraulics, disinfection, filtration, etc are built in.

Its basic characteristics are:
- six-lane public competition pool (probably with a separate teaching pool)
- deck-level (ie water level with surround; transfer channels to remove surface water)
- depth 1-2m
- surface area 325m^2
- water volume 487m^3

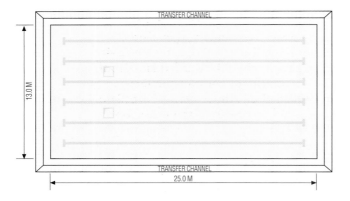

In Chapter 3 the typical pool will get plumbed in.

---

from 6 minutes for a commercial spa to 15 minutes for a residential spa, adequate filtration, and emptying at least once a week (even daily when loading is high). There are useful booklets on spa management, from SPATA and PHLS (see Bibliography). ISRM have courses specifically for spa operators.

Spas may have particular difficulties over the safety requirements for inlets and outlets. The main criterion for designers, manufacturers and operators is to take all reasonable precautions to prevent a bather, or part of a bather's body, becoming trapped. This should be based on the principles and methods given for swimming pools (see page 66).

Many spas will have hydrojet circulation, air induction bubbles, or some combination or variation of these; they may also be called whirlpool spas. A swimspa is either a small swimming pool with water agitation, or linked but separate swimming and spa pools. Jacuzzi is, strictly, a brand name for a particular spa pool - though it is sometimes incorrectly used as a generic name for spas. Unfiltered water may well be jetted into the spa. Even a spa running for display only should be disinfected, because of the infection risk.

Splash
See *Waterside splashdown*.

Teaching/Training
See *Learner*.

Waterslide splashdown
These are specially designed areas of water in which a rider completes the descent of a water slide or flume. If the splashdown pool shares its water circulation with that of a main pool, or has its own dedicated water distribution plant, the turnover must be able to cope with the highest bathing load it will have. Bather pollution will tend to be high for the amount of water involved.

Wave
These are usually incorporated in a leisure pool. Waves generated at one end (requiring a high free board) cross the pool to dissipate (usually) on a beach area. Surface water removal needs attention, as does water quality in the wave generation chambers.

Whirlpool
See *Spa*.

Chapter 3

Design and setup

Swimming and leisure pools are complicated constructions, making serious demands in terms of design, construction, operation and maintenance. This book is mainly about operation, which involves attention to maintenance; and less about construction. But design is critical to successful operation. Design comes first chronologically (though a brief and even a feasibility study may precede it), and needs to be considered by all the relevant professions. This applies equally to the design of new buildings and alterations to existing ones.

Water treatment systems are an integral part of the architectural, structural and mechanical design, and must be addressed from the very start of the project. Water treatment plant design must take into account:

- bathing load
- circulation rate
- turnover period
- choice of treatment system
- circulation hydraulics
- plant room
- filtration
- operation
- mains water quality, drainage and dilution.

The first three of these are dealt with in detail in this chapter. The rest are summarised here, and dealt with in detail later in the book - except for the last, already dealt with in the opening chapter

Overall, the design must conform to the appropriate guidelines for maintaining safety and the chemical and microbiological quality of the water. The HSE book, *Managing Health & Safety in Swimming Pools* (see Bibliography) is relevant here. Obviously the type of pool being planned - eg freeboard or deck-level - needs to be taken into account. Although this chapter cannot give advice on the details of design, it does indicate what areas need to be covered in a design brief. And there is advice about getting specialist design and contracting help.

BATHING LOAD

Bathing load (a measure of the number of people in the pool) is a difficult issue in pool water management - not least because there may be pressure to maximise income by overloading the pool. All pools should identify and maintain a realistic relationship between bathing numbers and pool and treatment plant capacity. For a new pool, the bathing load should be determined at the design stage. Circulation rate and treatment plant sizes can be derived from the bathing load. To check an existing pool, the bathing load calculated from its size (see below) should be compared with that derived from the turnover, treatment plant capacity etc - and the lower of the two should be the one followed.

Maximum bathing load
The many factors which determine the maximum bathing load for a pool include:

- water area - in terms of space for bathers to move around in, and physical safety
- depth of water - the deeper the water the more actual swimming there is and the more area a bather requires
- comfort
- pool type and bathing activity.

The first of these criteria - the safe area - is defined in the HSE book, *Managing Health & Safety in Swimming Pools*, as 1 bather per $3m^2$. (To prevent any confusion, such a figure is an area of water of, say, 3m by 1m - not, as occasionally misunderstood, 3m by 3m.) This gives a maximum bathing load over the whole pool, regardless of depth, and must in any case be modified in the light of local conditions. As far as designing and operating pools is concerned, including water treatment factors, practical experience here and abroad gives three maximum bathing load formulae that work:

Shallow water (under 1m)	**1 bather per 2.2m²**
Standing depth water (1-1.5m)	**1 bather per 2.7m²**
Deep water (over 1.5m)	**1 bather per 4m²**

The bathing load obtained using these formulae:

- is the maximum bathing load of the pool *at any one time (instantaneous bathing load)*
- should not be exceeded
- should be used when designing a pool and working out the circulation rate, etc.

The bathing load may need to be reduced operationally because of the capacity of the building, limitations of exits and entrances, the fitness of particular bathers, levels of supervision, etc. On the other hand, such considerations may (with the full understanding of the pool's manager) allow a higher bathing load.

Pool water treatment is a progressive process, so pollutants introduced to the water in one bathing period may not be completely removed until many hours later. On the other hand, water has a buffering capacity, so it can accommodate a certain buildup of pollutants before there is a problem. The instantaneous bathing load formulae take this into account - but after three to five hours' operation at that level, water quality could deteriorate. The buildup of suspended and colloidal matter, organic material and disinfection byproducts - all might produce uncomfortable bathing conditions.

So an *operational* bathing load must be established which takes into account the capacity of the system to maintain good water quality.

Operational daily bathing load

The bathing load of the pool *on a daily basis* is derived from the instantaneous bathing load - but must also take into account a number of variables, including bather cleanliness, the treatment system, the chemicals used, the operation of the whole system and the dilution rate. So it is not possible to give precise figures for maximum daily bather loads. But a good rule of thumb is to use 25-50% of the instantaneous bathing load multiplied by 12, assuming that the treatment plant operates - as it should (perhaps with reduced circulation at night) - for 24 hours a day.

If the daily bathing load is likely to exceed the figure estimated from this, then attention may need to be given to the treatment plant size, dilution or additional treatment such as ozone.

CIRCULATION RATE

The circulation rate is defined as the flow of water in m³/h to and from the pool through all the pipework and treatment system.

The appropriate circulation rate can be worked out according to a formula based on what, in practice, produces good water conditions:

$$\text{Circulation rate (m}^3/\text{h)} = \text{Instantaneous bathing load (bathers/m}^2) \times 1.7$$

The figure of 1.7 has no theoretical basis; it is arbitrary but works in practice.

There are, however, some types of pool where circulation rate cannot realistically be derived from bathing load - diving pools, for example. So turnover periods should be confirmed from the Table opposite.

The circulation rate and turnover period are related (see next section) and individually or together form the basis for sizing the circulation pumps and pipework (Chapter 11) and filtration plant (Chapter 12)

TURNOVER PERIOD

The time taken for a volume of water equivalent to the entire pool water volume to pass through the filters and treatment plant and back to the pool is called the turnover period. In principle, the shorter turnover period is, the more frequent and thorough is the pool water treatment.

The clarity of water which can be maintained in a pool depends on the relationship between bathing load, available water volume, turnover period (or circulation rate), hydraulics and the efficiency of the filters. If the filters continue to retain suspended matter and there is no further pollution, then continued filtration should ultimately give near-perfect clarity. In practice, turbidity must be removed in amounts at least equal to the added pollution. And filtration works progressively: pollution is removed over a series of passes through the filter.

Because of the tendency towards higher bathings loads, turnover periods of 4 hours or more - which were at one time considered satisfactory - are generally no longer adequate in public pools, as disinfectant residuals will decay below acceptable levels and turbidity will increase. Diving pools and other waters more than 2m deep are an exception to this, because bathing loads relative to water volume are inevitably lower.

There is a simple formula for deriving the turnover rate from the circulation rate established as in the previous section:

$$\text{Turnover period (h)} = \frac{\text{Water volume (m}^3)}{\text{Circulation rate (m}^3/\text{h)}}$$

Applying this formula should deliver the design circulation rate and form the basis for a satisfactory plant design.

Turnover periods and circulation rates must, however, also suit the particular type of pool. Turnover periods will vary from pool to pool, but should fall into the ranges in the Table on this page. The turnover period indicated there for a particular pool may be shorter than that calculated from the formula above. If so, the Table should be followed, and a revised circulation rate worked out from the formula:

$$\text{Circulation rate (m}^3/\text{h)} = \frac{\text{Water volume (m}^3)}{\text{Turnover period (h)}}$$

Note Ideally, turnover in a modern pool - be it leisure or conventional - can and should be designed to vary in different parts of the pool; longer periods in deep areas, shorter where it is shallow.

Where pools have **moveable floors**, the volume is reduced as the floor is raised. The turnover must be appropriate to the biggest bathing load the pool will have - ie at its shallowest. If a moveable floor is to be fitted to an existing pool, the hydraulics and turnover must be thoroughly reviewed first.

The turnover periods listed in the Table for **waterslide splashdown pools** refer to pools which have a separate filtration and circulation system. But such pools may be incorporated into the main pool's system. Then, as with moveable floors, the turnover must be appropriate to the biggest bathing load both pools together will have; the circulation system and plant design must be sized accordingly. Adding on a waterside splash pool to an existing system makes a new demand on the system: it is essential that the

---

Turnover periods for different types of pool

Competition pools 50m long	3 - 4h
Conventional public pools up to 25m long with a 1m shallow end	2h 30 min - 3h
Diving pools	4 - 8h
Hydrotherapy pools	30min - 1h
Leisure water bubble pools	5 - 20min
Leisure waters up to 0.5m deep	10 - 45min
Leisure waters 0.5-1m deep	30min - 1h 15min
Leisure waters 1-1.5m deep	1 - 2h
Leisure waters over 1.5m deep	2h - 2h 30min
Spas	5 - 15min
Teaching/learner/training pools	30min - 1h 30min
Waterslide splash pools	30min - 1h

new circulation and the existing filtration be assessed to ensure that the extra load will not threaten good water quality. Most waterslides have runout channels instead of splashdown pools. In this case an allowance should be made for the ride's water treatment - equivalent to splashdown pool standards, and certainly not less than a treatment circulation rate of $30\text{m}^3/\text{h}$ per waterslide.

School pools (and hotel and health club pools) may be able to have a longer turnover period than an equivalent public pool. In general, where there are strict limits on loading and on the time the pools are used, designers can depart from the guidelines in this book. But care must be taken to match plant capacity to the water volume, to take account of peak periods - perhaps when the pool is used by the general public. Before general public use (dual use) is introduced, operators must be sure that the pool has the capacity for it. The design bathing load of school pools (and others) should be well known - usefully, stated on a plate on a plant room wall, and enforced by management at the entrance. A Department for Education & Employment booklet (see Bibliography) is helpful for those responsible for school pools.

CHOICE OF TREATMENT SYSTEM

The water treatment system should be chosen on the basis of many considerations - in particular, the nature of the water supply, the type of pool, its likely bathing loads, the quality aimed for in the water and the pool hall atmosphere, and the skills available to

The typical pool

The typical pool from Chapter 2 is now fitted with a balance tank (to collect surface water from the transfer channels) and an automatic make-up water system.

Calculations of the typical pool's bathing load, circulation rate and dilution are based on the formulae in this chapter.

Instantaneous bathing load
162.5m² of water depth 1-1.5m @ 1 bather/2.7m² = 60 bathers
162.5m² of water depth 1.5-2m @ 1 bather/4m² = 41 bathers
Total 101 bathers

Circulation rate
Instantaneous bathing load 101 x 1.7 = 172m³/h

Turnover period

$$\frac{\text{Water volume } 487m^3}{\text{Circulation rate } 172m^3/h} = 2.83h$$

Confirm 2.83h using table on page 21

Dilution
Daily bathing load = 101 x 50% x 12 = 600 bathers
Diluting @ 30 litres per bather per day (recommendation page 12) gives 18,000 litres, or 126m³ a week
Filter backwashing (once or twice a week) would dump 30m³/week
Evaporation would lose 18m³ a week
Total 48m³
So a further 78m³ a week might need to be dumped - some of it, ideally, in pre-swim showers.

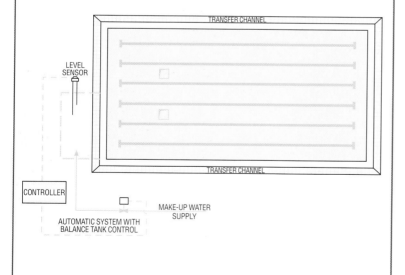

Pre-swim showers are fitted in Chapter 4

operate the system. Those responsible for deciding on a treatment system may want to call on the experience of other pool managers, operators, etc - particularly if they have experience of the local water supply.

Chapter 5 deals in detail with the choice of disinfectant (as well as refinements like ozone) and Chapters 6-9 with the mechanics of disinfection. Water treatment systems have three key elements - chemical dosing, circulation (pumps, pipework, etc) and filtration. These issues are dealt with in chapters 10-12. Chapter 13 deals with the detailed monitoring of chemicals in use. The choice of treatment system must also take into account the safety of the various disinfectant and associated chemicals - see Chapters 16-18. Disinfection in relation to the threat (sometimes imagined) from microorganisms are dealt with in Chapter 14.

The choice of chemicals will have design implications - see opposite page.

CIRCULATION HYDRAULICS

The purpose of giving close attention to circulation and hydraulics is to ensure that the whole pool is adequately served. Treated water must get to all parts of the pool; polluted water must be removed - especially from areas most used and most polluted by bathers. If not, even good water treatment may not give good water quality. Conversely, first-rate circulation hydraulics may allow an over-stretched water treatment system to produce good pool water.

As detailed in Chapter 11, the design and positioning of inlets, outlets and surface water withdrawal are crucial. A deck-level system (pool water level with the surrounds), with a balance tank and pool surround collecting channels, is particularly efficient: almost all of the total circulation rate can be removed from the surface, where pollution is greatest. Leisure pools, particularly if they are to have a freeboard area for water features such as waves, may allow only a partial deck-level system.

Given a circulation rate worked out by the formulae described earlier in this chapter, and taking into account the water velocity and inlet and outlet issues in Chapter 11, the very

Safeguarding the fabric of the building

There are various ways in which the use of pool water chemicals can have a damaging effect on the fabric of pool buildings. Some of these are dealt in more detail later in this book as they come up. But it may be useful in terms of design to gather them together here (with cross references).

Perhaps the most dramatic is the stress corrosion cracking of stainless steel, seemingly provoked by disinfection byproducts. At its worst, this has caused the failure of struts supporting ceilings. New constructions need not use stainless steel for structural applications. In any case, using stainless steel in pool buildings demands close attention to the choice of grades of stainless steel, and good inspection and maintenance techniques. (See Bibliography for a free publication on the subject.)

In general, well chosen stainless steel elements in and around the pool water are easier to maintain and less likely to give corrosion problems.

There have been discoveries of destruction of steel in the reinforced concrete making up the pool tank itself. This is presumed to be the result of chloride attack following penetration of the grout and/or tiles lining the pool, or the pool lining. The extent of the problem, and its solutions, are not clear.

Grout attack is a problem. Some pools have had to have grout expensively replaced within a few years. The cause is not clear. Low calcium hardness has been blamed, but the evidence is equivocal. It may be more to do with unsuitable grout, acid attack, water movement, cleaners, working and application standards, changing tile sizes, etc. See page 79 for more details.

It is well established that sulphate levels over 360mg/l will attack grout. If such levels cannot be avoided, sulphate-resistant Portland cement and epoxy grouts will be necessary. See page 80 for more details.

Hardness deposits can be troublesome - not least on flumes.

Great care must be taken not to damage the pool tank when the pool has to be emptied and refilled (see page 127), and when the water is heated from cold (page 115).

important details of circulation hydraulics (including pipework) can then be specified.

PLANT ROOM

Plant room design should consider five key issues - location, size, access, segregation and environment. These issues, as far as delivery and storage of chemicals are concerned, are mostly dealt with in Chapters 17 and 18. There are clear design issues.

The **location** of the filtration and water treatment system in relation to the pool critically affects hydraulic design. Circulation pumps should, ideally, operate under flooded suction conditions and be sited near the balance tank, and near the extraction points from the pool. (If the pumps have to be some distance from the balance tank, increasing the suction pipe size may improve pump performance.) If the plant room has to be at pool surround level, a pump pit will give flooded suction conditions. If there is no balance tank, the connection between pool water and pumps must be designed to keep the system free of air entrainment.

The **size** of the plant room (water treatment plant only) will typically be between 15 and 30% of the pool water area (depending on the treatment method used). It should be sized to ensure good **access**, both to the plant room itself and for plant room equipment operation, delivery of chemicals, maintenance and replacement. It is difficult, in most plant rooms, to allow for the removal of complete filters; instead, they will usually be removed in

A typical plant room

sections, and replacements put together *in situ*. Filter media may need to be replaced every 5-7 years, filters themselves after perhaps 25 years.

Certain equipment needs **segregation**. For example, chemicals should be stored in separate, secure rooms. Electrical control panels, chemical control units, ozone generators etc should be in clean, dry areas away from chemical stores, and on raised concrete work plinths. See Chapter 18

Certain plant items demand a specific **environment**. For example, there are important requirements (under COSHH) for ventilating ozone plant and chemical mixing areas; most electrical items will require limits on plant room air temperature and humidity. There is also a requirement for effective and suitable plant room ventilation in the Workplace (Health, Safety and Welfare) Regulations 1992.

FILTRATION

Filters are responsible for removing particulate matter (suspended and colloidal) from the pool water. They should run continuously, 24 hours a day, to deal with the pollution arising from bathers, but can have a reduced flow rate at night if good water quality can still be maintained. If filters do not work effectively, or are not big enough for the job, turbidity (generally, suspended solids) will not be adequately reduced whatever the turnover period. Indeed, an inefficient filter yielding a filtrate containing suspended matter may increase turbidity rather than improve the clarity of the water. Given adequate filtration, however, the shorter the turnover period, the better the rate that suspended solids are removed.

Chapter 12 deals with the specification of filters. In summary, medium-rate pressure sand filters are recommended for all non-domestic pools including those hotel and school pools which are subject to loading demands similar to those of conventional public pools. The filtration system design will be linked to that for circulation pumps, heating, associated pipework, valves, etc. The linings needed on mild steel filters can be a particular problem if the materials and their application are not properly addressed (see page 74).

OPERATION

The contract with consultant or contractor should ensure that the water treatment contractor provides training for the plant operator both during commissioning of the plant and once it is operating. And the operator should be present for the critical process of commissioning. The pool management should also be involved at this stage. Commissioning should include fully checking the system for health and safety requirements. This should cover plant room issues, but also the safety and supervision of any water features.

The water treatment design brief should require the provision of operation and maintenance manuals (including plant and pipe layout drawings). As well as detailing how the system is to be operated, these should list the daily, weekly, monthly and annual checks which are necessary. They can also usefully contain details of the emergency and ordering procedures which indicate the precise names of chemicals used, to prevent errors. Management and training are dealt with in Chapter 20 inspection and maintenance in Chapter 21.

DESIGN BRIEF

Water treatment is just one factor within the design of what may be a multi-use leisure complex. The starting point for design is a full assessment, by the client responsible for providing the pool, of the needs and demand involved, taking into account existing provision etc. Depending on the particular project, there may have been a strategy prepared, a multi-disciplinary project team appointed, a feasibility study commissioned, and decisions taken on location and finance. By the end of this stage, a project manager and an architect experienced in pool design should, ideally, have been appointed. They will then work together to produce a design brief. Consultation on the design brief should include the local authority if is to be the enforcing authority for a new installation.

A design brief is a broad description of what is to be provided within the design; it is not a specification. The purpose of the brief is to establish the performance requirements of the design and hence a framework within which the detailed design work can progress. The starting point is a decision on the type of facility required - eg the type and amount of use envisaged; swimming or leisure; moveable floors/booms to convert competition/diving pools into learner/leisure; other joint-use arrangements; possible shared treatment plant for different pools.

The design brief, preferably accompanied by a basic schematic diagram and system layout, should cover the parameters dealt with throughout this book, and in particular the water treatment design brief issues listed on this page. It can also usefully cover essential operational and staffing factors.

Construction (Design and Management) Regulations 1994

These CDM regulations, made under the Health and Safety at Work, Etc Act 1974, place specific requirements on the designer - whether an architect, engineer, contractor or from some other professional discipline. They have a responsibility to assess site hazards and deal with them where possible; and pass on information to keep workers safe and reduce accidents on construction sites.

Under the regulations designers have both a statutory and a civil liability; and under the former there is no insurance against liability.

The designer's duties can be summarised:
- advise clients on their responsibilities under the regulations
- co-operate with other designers
- co-operate with the planning supervisor
- design for safety
- keep records
- provide information for the health and safety plan
- provide information for the health and safety file
- choose competent contractors and subcontractors
- comply with quality assurance systems where they apply.

As part of the design process, hazards must be identified at each stage of the design and the appropriate risk assessments done. All of this must be recorded and details provided for the health and safety plan/file as appropriate.

The planning supervisor on a project, who is responsible for co-ordination of design, should ensure that those responsible for building and engineering design consider health and safety (including that of swimmers). The planning supervisor also advises the client, and:
- ensures that a health and safety plan is prepared
- reviews the construction stage of the health and safety plan
- ensures that a health and safety file is prepared
- delivers the health and safety file to the client.

DESIGN BRIEF ISSUES

These issues are presented here simply as headings; where appropriate, there are references to details elsewhere in the book.

It is unlikely that one person - consultant, architect, manager, pool operator or whatever - would be fully conversant with all these technical issues. But anybody with some responsibility for a new building or alteration of an existing one does need to be aware that these technical issues must be taken into account. (Maintenance, too - not dealt with here, but summarised in Chapter 21- needs to be included.)

Bathing load, circulation rate, turnover

Bathing load affects circulation rate; this, with pool volume, governs turnover period; the two together determine the size of filtration plant etc, and affect the selection of the water treatment system. So these issues are central - see page 19.

Water treatment

Chapters 6, 7, 8 and 9 deal in detail with disinfection; Chapters 13, 14 and 15 with maintaining good water quality. In design terms this means considering:
- source water characteristics - bearing in mind that these may change
- pool type
- pool temperature
- removal of suspended and colloidal matter
- disinfection and oxidising agents
- coagulants
- pH adjustment
- water balance
- fresh water dilution
- effects on air quality
- plant size and operation

- plant personnel; training
- water testing and recording
- plant monitoring and control
- energy and operation costs
- guidelines on water quality.

Hydraulics

The design of water movement (mostly dealt with in Chapter 11) demands attention to:

- pool size and shape (including profile)
- size, number and location (including safety considerations) of pool water inlets and outlets
- size and routing of circulation pipework
- size and location of balance tank
- water circulation within the balance tank
- transfer channels
- pumping and location of pump sump (if needed)
- design and correct sizing of the filtration plant, including filters and filtration rates (Chapter 12)
- integration of water features
- moving floors and booms
- effect of evaporation (normal and induced by water features) on relative humidity in the pool hall
- effect of water movement on noise levels in the pool hall.

Plant room

Many issues need to be considered at the design stage (some of them dealt with in Chapters 17 and 18):

- size and location of plant room, taking into account filter specifications, the scale of other water treatment plant, and the need for short, flooded suction pipework
- location of other plant items and ductwork
- plant layout for ease of operation and maintenance
- interfaces and co-ordination with other building elements - including ventilation intakes (well away from plant room and chemical stores)
- access for plant replacement/refurbishment
- access for chemical deliveries, including safety considerations
- secure bunded storage areas for chemicals
- washwater and drainage requirements
- health and safety requirements
- plant room environment relating to temperature, humidity, ventilation and noise

- builders' work requirements
- electrical requirements (the current IEE regulations).

General environment

There are a number of such design issues that affect water quality:

- movement of people
- how much of the operation is inside and how much outside the building
- pre-swim hygiene (Chapter 4)
- tile finishes, etc (which can affect algal growth)
- how floors are arranged on poolside, in changing rooms, etc - including drainage
- cleaning around the pools - especially if there can be a separate route for draining cleaning products (Chapter 22)
- separation of function in changing rooms, so that shoes don't get wet and spread dirt
- how far polluting features (like flumes) spill into main pools (say, via waterfalls)

SPECIALIST HELP

Building or substantially refurbishing a swimming pool, to be a success, demands a proper understanding of the distinction between design and installation. It is also important that the responsibility for issues of design and installation is clearly identified at the beginning of the project.

Who designs?

Water treatment design requires specialist engineering knowledge, which needs to be recruited at the same time as the architect and structural and environmental services engineers. That knowledge, which is critical to producing a satisfactory design, is available from two sources:

- consultants - who can provide independent specialist advice and who are appointed as full members of the design team
- contractors - who can work to a consultant's brief, or to their own or a client's.

Normally, an architect would be the lead consultant - co-ordinating design, construction, building services, etc; a specialist building services engineer would advise on water treatment design and liaise with specialist companies before tender.

Choosing a water treatment consultant

A water treatment consultant with pool experience will develop the brief, produce a competent design, detailed drawings and specification, monitor the installation work on site and oversee final commissioning. When competitive tenders are needed, the consultant should be particularly valuable in ensuring that they are based on an equivalent level of specification and scope of work.

It is important that the water treatment consultant belongs to a recognised engineering institute and is not linked to any particular manufacturers or suppliers. Lists of water treatment consultants are available from professional and other institutes such as ISRM and CIBSE (addresses page 137). References should be pursued, and the consultants' skill and experience in water treatment verified by interview.

Choosing a water treatment contractor

If the client has a good design brief or specification, then a water treatment contractor can be appointed to design as well as install the plant. The choice of contractor then becomes particularly important.

In any case, the contractor must be responsible for the supply, installation and commissioning of the system, and for incorporating equipment from reputable manufacturers. There is no single method for finding the right contractor. But there are at least five useful pointers for selecting contractors (and manufacturers).

- Members of trade and professional affiliations (British Water, ISRM, CIBSE, SPATA etc - addresses page 137) should be considered first. The first three are more appropriate for the public pool market.
- Contractors may offer accredited quality assurance - perhaps to ISO EN 9000. Where contractors provide a design warranty, they should be qualified to Part 1 of this standard. This should imply a quality system, though not necessarily a quality product.
- Previous work can be checked by visiting installations and by taking up references from clients, architects and engineers. References should comment on design ability, performance during contract, reliability of equipment recommended and used, commissioning and staff training record, standard of operating and

maintenance manuals, and after-sales service.
- A long and successful record of quality work is a positive indication.
- Good contractors, like good consultants and good suppliers, will be familiar with this book.

Chapter 4

Pollution and hygiene

Pollution is introduced almost continuously into the water of swimming pools. Even the mains water that supplies them may contain substances that affect pool water quality (see Chapter 1). But the main source of pollution is the bathers themselves. Whatever the source of pollution, it should be minimised and dealt with by appropriate water treatment, including disinfection and the other processes described in this book.

The specific issues raised by microbiological contamination are dealt with in Chapter 14. This chapter identifies the other sources of pollution, assesses their threat and describes how they may be minimised.

POLLUTION FROM BATHERS

Any substance associated with the human body may be introduced to pool water by bathers. There are, broadly, three categories.

Tissues and excretions
The main culprits are sweat, urine, mucus from the nose and chest, saliva, hair and scales from the skin, and faecal matter. These are pollutants in themselves, and most contain microorganisms (bacteria and viruses).

Urination, sometimes involuntary, certainly does happen in swimming pools. And most bathers will lose significant amounts of sweat in the exercise of swimming - particularly in the higher temperature pool water that has become common (see page 116). This is a good reason for discouraging access from a sauna to the main pool. The reaction between disinfectant and the breakdown products of urea in sweat and urine is the main cause of high combined chlorine residuals (chloramines, see page 38) in the water, which contribute to eye and skin irritation. Some of these chlorinous compounds pass into the air, producing irritant fumes in the atmosphere above the pool. These can affect both bathers and poolside staff.

Urea also adds considerably to the costs of maintaining the quality of the water. More water and air changes are needed, so energy saving measures may be compromised in order to maintain the comfort of bathers and staff.

Dirt
Clearly, dirt of all sorts normally collects on the body before bathing. Open-air pools pose a particular problem as dust, leaves, grass, soil, bird droppings, insects, etc can contaminate pool water directly as well as via swimmers. Chapter 22 deals with cleaning in detail.

Cosmetics
Materials such as powders, creams, lotions and oils are a rich source of pollutants, many of them imposing a significant challenge to the water treatment system.

PRE-SWIM HYGIENE

In some other European countries it is quite routine (even compulsory) to shower before a swim; a swimming cap may even be required as well. In the UK, showers are more likely to be seen as a means of washing off the pool water after a swim. It is ironic, of course, that the disinfectant swimmers want to remove by

Where pollution ends up in the pool

DISSOLVED POLLUTION
• URINE
• PERSPIRATION
• COSMETICS
• SUNTAN LOTION

SUSPENDED POLLUTION
MINUTE CHEMICAL PARTICLES PRODUCED BY CHEMICAL REACTIONS IN WATER TREATMENT

SURFACE POLLUTION
• HAIR
• DUST
• BODY GREASE
• EXCRETA FROM NOSE AND MOUTH
• FLOATING DEBRIS
• GRASS

INSOLUBLES
• FLUFF
• DIRT (SOIL/STONES)
• PRECIPITATED CHEMICALS
• SAND FROM FILTERS

showering is there in such quantities in order to deal with the body pollution introduced by swimmers who do not shower first.

Although the value of pre-swim showering might seem self-evident, a simple series of trials by PWTAG confirmed this and gave some idea of the extent of the benefit. Schoolchildren swam after shower, footbath or neither. Controlled showers at different stages of the process measured the amount of dirt, sweat and microbial debris. Results were clear.

- Pre-swim showering does remove significant amounts of dirt and bacteria that otherwise end up in the pool. Up to two-thirds of the sweat products, and a third of the bacteria, are removed.
- Even without soaping, showering removes much of the pollution.
- A shower removes five times the pollution that a footbath does.

So if pre-swim showering were the norm, pool water would be cleaner, easier to disinfect with less chemicals and thus more pleasant to swim in. There would, too, be money saved on chemicals (off-set to some extent by the extra cost of heating shower water). Important recommendations about footbaths, showers, toilets and bather education follow from this.

SHOWERS

The best system is separate **pre-swim showers**. They should be on the route from changing rooms to pool, and supplied with water at most 2 degrees Celsius above pool water temperature. They can be continuous to encourage use. Pre-swim showers must run to waste. New pools at least should be designed so that pre-swim showers are supplied from the pool water circulation system itself. Operators should first be satisfied - through a COSHH assessment - that the water supplied for the showers is microbiologically satisfactory. The shower water will have a disinfectant residual, which should help prevent microbial growth in the pipework and shower heads, as well as being helpful in the showering itself. The replacement fresh water becomes part of the pool water dilution system. If the pool has an automatic make-up water system, shower water should be taken after the filtration process and boosted on a ring-main system.

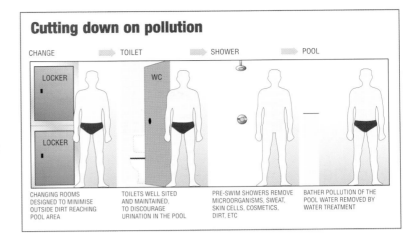

Cutting down on pollution

CHANGE ⟹ TOILET ⟹ SHOWER ⟹ POOL

LOCKER

LOCKER

WC

CHANGING ROOMS DESIGNED TO MINIMISE OUTSIDE DIRT REACHING POOL AREA

TOILETS WELL SITED AND MAINTAINED, TO DISCOURAGE URINATION IN THE POOL

PRE-SWIM SHOWERS REMOVE MICROORGANISMS, SWEAT, SKIN CELLS, COSMETICS, DIRT, ETC

BATHER POLLUTION OF THE POOL WATER REMOVED BY WATER TREATMENT

Post-swim showers can be on a different, return route from pool to changing-rooms. They should be supplied with fresh water (stored at 60°C, piped at 50°C and then mixed to around 40°C), run to waste. There should be provision for soap and shampoo and, ideally, cubicles for privacy and nude showering.

New pools should consider incorporating these principles in their design. This and other changing-room issues are dealt with in the Sport England handbook listed in the Bibliography (page 138). For existing pools, achieving these arrangements presents a challenge; substantial refurbishment has to be considered. There is little doubt, though, that the benefits all round will be worth the effort.

FOOTBATHS

These are no longer considered important. Their role in dealing with verrucas and other foot infections is now considered largely irrelevant (see Chapter 14). Showers do their cleaning work more effectively, and bring extra benefits. If there really is no alternative, however, especially in an outdoor pool, a properly maintained footbath (or foot spray) is better than nothing. There must in any case be some barrier between outdoor dirt and the pool (while still allowing wheelchair access).

TOILETS

These should be provided where they can be conveniently used before entering the pool; explanatory notices and posters should be prominently displayed. Everyone - but children in particular - should be educated to use the toilets before bathing to minimise involuntary urination in the pool. Babies should not be allowed to swim in nappies; instead, they should be encouraged to empty their bladders before they swim and wear special baby costumes. (See also page 93.) Pool management should include frequent inspection and cleaning of toilets.

EDUCATION

Swimmers need to understand the importance to them of pre-swim hygiene: it helps provide more comfortable water. The PWTAG poster, *You don't want your eyes to sting, so use the loo before you swim*, also advocates pre-swim showering. But no amount of education, or persuasion - even rules - will work unless there are enough showers and toilets, conveniently positioned and well maintained.

The subject of infection, dealt with in Chapter 14, also raises educational issues - see particularly page 89.

The typical pool

The typical pool now has pre-swim showers running off pool water, as first suggested in Chapter 3.
Water consumption per showerhead - 0.5m³/h
Weekly water consumption of 4 showerheads, 6 hours a day,
7 days a week - 84m³
This is very near the 78m³ that Chapter 3 decided the typical pool might need to dump for water quality.

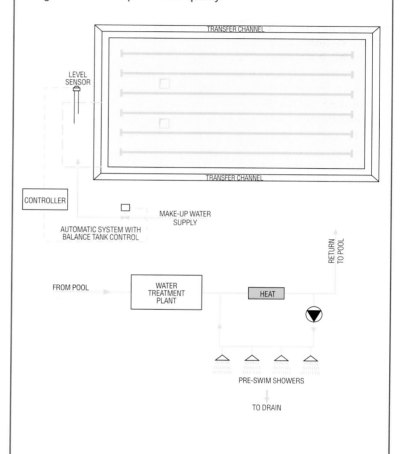

So far so good. Next, disinfection needs to go in - Chapter 5.

Choosing a disinfectant

There are many ways to disinfect a pool, and the choice can seem complicated. The various pressures on those responsible for the choice will not necessarily help. Chapters 6-10 deal with disinfectant use in more detail. This chapter clarifies the choice - by emphasising the key areas of:

- compatibility with the source water supply (for fill and make-up)
- type and size of pool
- bathing load, etc
- operation - supervision, management
- comparative costs.

The crucial issue of safety, however, is dealt with first here.

CHEMICAL SAFETY

Under the Control of Substances Hazardous to Health Regulations 1994 (COSHH), every employer has a responsibility to assess the risks associated with hazardous substances in the work place and to take adequate steps to eliminate or control those risks. This applies to all substances that can adversely affect health, including those listed as toxic, harmful, irritant or corrosive under the Chemicals (Hazard, Information and Packaging for Supply) Regulations 1994 (CHIP2).

These regulations cover the majority of swimming pool chemicals, hence the need for special care choosing and using such materials. The first step is to consider only those disinfectants approved on safety grounds by the relevant government committee; then, based on a clear understanding of what they contain, to prepare a risk assessment under the terms of the two regulations above. The technical basis for this is is dealt with in Chapter 16, and the management considerations in Chapter 20.

The review of disinfectants in this chapter takes safety into account as well as effectiveness.

DEALING WITH SOURCE WATER

The better suited the disinfectant is to the source water, the more efficient will be the disinfection and the fewer chemicals of all sorts will need to be used. So it certainly makes sense, when choosing a disinfectant, to take into account the nature of the mains water supply. Its hardness and alkalinity, particularly, will affect how easily the different disinfectants work. Dealing sympathetically with the raw water is better than struggling to change it into something it is not. It will certainly tend to involve using less chemicals.

It is normally possible, for example, to adjust the chemical treatment of soft water to suit the requirements of any disinfectant; but more difficult adjusting hard water. And the acidity or alkalinity of the disinfectant will have an effect on subsequent pH adjustment.

It is generally good practice, where possible, to use the makeup water to neutralise partially the acidity (or alkalinity) of the disinfectant. Below is a guide - bearing in mind that many source waters will be somewhere between these two extremes.

Matching the water - the rough guide

With soft waters, typically hardness under 50mg/l $CaCO_3$ alkalinity under 30mg/l $CaCO_3$ pH value easily influenced

An alkaline disinfectant is the likeliest - sodium hypochlorite plus calcium chloride to increase hardness a little, or calcium hypochlorite; to lower the pH value, a gentle acid such as carbonic acid (from carbon dioxide).

With hard waters, typically hardness over 250mg/l $CaCO_3$ alkalinity over 150mg/l $CaCO_3$ pH value stable

The disinfectant should be one that operates well at the pH of the mains water. Chlorine gas (with the proper safeguards) is worth considering for large pools, trichloroisocyanuric acid for smaller pools and lidos; otherwise, hypochlorite. Avoid carbon dioxide for pH value control.

The choice of disinfectant will also take into account other local factors.

One last caution: hypochlorites tend to push up pH values, so disinfectant activity is reduced. Adding acid to reduce pH, if not precise, may mean alkalinity needs to be increased. And so on. Adding chemicals to reduce the levels of other chemicals increases dissolved solids, is expensive and tends to reduce margins for error, so problems are likelier. Understanding the issue should guard against getting into that vicious circle.

CHLORINE-BASED DISINFECTANTS

In terms of effectiveness in use (as long as the nature of the source water has been taken into account in the choice), there is little to choose between chlorine in gas or hypochlorite form. Bacteria are killed and pollutants oxidised by hypochlorous acid and hypochlorite ions - together known as free residual chlorine - in both cases. But there are other relevant factors.

Chlorine gas
Liquefied chlorine gas is the purest form of chlorine disinfectant - the benchmark against which are measured the replacements that resulted from the government's 1978 recommendation to discontinue its use because of the danger of gassing accidents. (For example, calcium hypochlorite has up to 5% insolubles; sodium hypochlorite contains some caustic soda; both add to the total dissolved solids in pool water.) Chapters 10, 17 and 18 give details of how chlorine gas may be effectively and safely dosed, delivered, and stored - but even the system now recommended - a separate, totally enclosed store with a fail-safe dosing system - has the potential, given operator error, of a life-threatening accident. Nevertheless, chlorine gas has demonstrated its ability to work well in recent installations, where all relevant precautions are taken, and the necessary approvals granted.

Hypochlorites
Sodium and calcium hypochlorites are also capable of producing dangerous levels of chlorine gas if accidentally mixed with acid. But it would be difficult for sufficient acid to mix with bulk stored hypochlorite to cause the release of chlorine gas in quantities as great as from a full cylinder of chlorine gas. Again,

chapters 10, 17 and 18 give details for safe use, delivery and storage - including the advantages of storing in bulk on site. Sodium hypochlorite has a maximum strength of 15% w/w as available chlorine. Sodium hypochlorite can be *generated* by passing an electric current through sodium chloride solution - see page 40.

Calcium hypochlorite comes in sealed plastic or steel drums, in different solid formats. Automated transfer and mixing systems that minimise handling, and thus exposure of operatives to the chemical, are safer than those requiring manual mixing of the solids in day tanks. But in practice, the regular cleaning needed, and other maintenance problems, may cancel out that advantage.

Calcium hypochlorite comes in different strengths; 68% as available chlorine is the highest concentration that should be used for pools, on safety grounds. Calcium hypochlorite has three specific hazards.

- It reacts violently with organic materials (chlorinated isocyanurates or cleaners, for example - even cola drinks) by spontaneous combustion, explosion and the production of toxic gases. Even a trace of, say, oil can be enough. And, like sodium hypochlorite, it reacts dangerously with acids. So staff must be aware that it needs to be stored and used with care.
- Particularly in its powder form, irritant dust can be breathed in during handling and affect the lungs quite severely. Even with granular and tablet forms, personal protection equipment should be used.
- If heated, it produces chlorine gas.

Calcium hypochlorite is particularly suited to soft waters that are also low in natural calcium.

CHLORINATED ISOCYANURATES

These disinfectants are an indirect source of free chlorine residual, via an organic reserve (see page 41 for details). Sodium dichloroisocyanurate dihydrate and trichloroisocyanuric acid produce a chlorine residual which, in theory, disinfects as well as that from inorganic chlorine-based disinfectants. But the relationship between that residual and the level of cyanuric acid is very critical and can be difficult to maintain. If it is lost because cyanuric acid levels become too high, UK government-sponsored research has established that unsatisfactory microbiological conditions can result. So they are not suited to the variations in bathing loads usually found in large public pools. They have a place in the disinfection of small, lightly loaded public pools, especially in hard water areas.

Great care must be exercised to prevent contact with hypochlorite, especially calcium hypochlorite, as this can cause a very violent explosion. Chlorinated isocyanurates also need to be stored separately from acids.

BROMINE-BASED DISINFECTANTS

There are basically three bromine systems - elemental liquid bromine, bromochlorodimethylhydantoin (BCDMH) and sodium bromide plus hypochlorite. This book does not deal with them in the same detail as chlorine-based disinfectants, because:

- they are not widely used for conventional public pools in the UK; and there are doubts about the evidence for their effectiveness, compared to chlorine-based disinfectants
- chlorine-based disinfectants are of proven effectiveness, given a properly designed, operated and maintained pool water system, with well-trained operators
- if these elements are not in place, it is normally a mistake to look beyond chlorine-based disinfectants for a remedy.

If, however, design etc are satisfactory, bromine-based products may be considered, perhaps because the pool is very lightly used, or space is tight. All tend to give a greener pool water than chlorine-based disinfectants.

Elemental bromine disinfects and oxidises in a similar way to chlorine. It is more difficult to transport, handle and use safely - and is considered to be a greater hazard generally. Bromide levels in the pool (as high as 1,000mg/l have been found) raise a question, given bromide's known tranquillising effects. As it is very little used, this book gives no more details on its use.

BCDMH and sodium bromide plus hypochlorite are dealt with in Chapters 7 and 8.

Bromochlorodimethylhydantoin

BCDMH is an organic compound that disinfects with a free bromine residual. Like the chlorinated isocyanurates, failure to maintain the correct relationship between the disinfectant residual and the organic component can result in unsatisfactory microbiological conditions. The level of dimethylhydantoin in the water must be limited. On the other hand, BCDMH is relatively innocuous in storage, easy to dose, and often does not need pH correction.

There have been reports in medical journals of skin irritation (itch and rash) of a type not found in chlorine pools. Although the relevant government committee now advises checking for skin irritation with all disinfectants, there is considerable evidence that it is more of a problem with BCDMH. It is not clear whether this is due to bad management or something unique to BCDMH - but it does mean extra vigilance in operating to the guidelines in this book and from the manufacturer.

Sodium bromide plus hypochlorite

This is a proprietary system which involves the conversion of bromide to free bromine residual. Sodium bicarbonate solution is also added as a buffer to the hypochlorite day tank. The bromide level has to be checked and maintained, or a troublesome mixture of byproducts can be produced. Claims that irritant byproducts are fewer than with hypochlorite have not been substantiated. Bromoforms appear to be formed in greater quantities than the equivalent chlorine compounds. Any increased risk from this is largely theoretical, but nevertheless worth avoiding.

OZONE AND ULTRAVIOLET

Ozone gas and UV radiation are different from the disinfectants reviewed so far in this chapter. They are plant-room treatments that purify the circulating water, making subsequent disinfection easier, but without leaving a residual in the pool water. As a result of the purification, a lower-than-usual level of free chlorine residual (from chlorine gas or hypochlorite) can disinfect the pool water.

Ozone kills microorganisms and helps limit levels of organic and inorganic byproducts. It is generated *in situ*, and though its generation demands extra space, there are no storage issues; but it is toxic in significant atmospheric concentrations, so excess must be removed within the treatment system. And there must be careful training for pool staff in the safe operation of the ozone equipment, and good ventilation in the plant room. In general, the level of competence for staff operating ozone must be higher than average.

UV radiation of pool water will inactivate microorganisms and help break down some pollutants. It is a less powerful purifier than ozone, and does not allow as low a level of free chlorine residual to disinfect the pool water. There are relatively few UV installations in pools, so its effectiveness is still to be established.

Comparative costs

COMPETITION POOL
Size 25m x13m
Estimated bathing load 200,000 per annum
Surface area 325m^2
Volume 500m^3
Turnover 2.5h
Circulation rate 200m^2/h

Capital costs
Water treatment (filtration, sodium hypochlorite) £120,000
Plus ozone £55,000 (UV £30,000)
Building £1,200,000 (1,150 m^2; building : water ratio 3.5:1)
Water treatment is 10% of capital costs

Running costs per annum
Chemicals £4,500
Water £5,000 (@ approx £1/m^3 including discharge)
Energy £30,000 (plus ozone £4,000, UV £2,000)
Total of chemicals, water, energy £39,500
Chemicals are 11% of running costs
Water is 13% of running costs

LEISURE POOL
(including bubble pool, etc)
Estimated bathing load 700,000 per annum
Surface area 650m^2
Volume 600m^3
Turnover 1.15 h (average)
Circulation rate 521m^3/h

Capital costs
Water treatment (filtration, sodium hypochlorite, O$_3$) £310,000
Building £3,750,000 (3,000m^2; building : water ratio 4.6:1)
Water treatment is 8% of capital costs

Running costs per annum
Chemicals £10,000
Water £21,000 (@ approx £1/m^3 including discharge)
Energy £70,000 (including ozone @ £5,000)
Total of chemicals, water, energy £101,000
Chemicals are 10% of running costs
Water is 21% of running costs
Ozone energy is 5% of running costs

COSTS

When planning disinfection, it is worth looking at its capital and running costs - in particular, perhaps, as a proportion of the totals for the pool building. The costs in this section are estimated comparative capital and running costs for a number of typical pool types and sizes. Typical estimated total building costs and overall energy and water usage and costs are included for comparative purposes.

Capital costs are based on Sport England net building cost data and exclude any external works, land charges, legal costs, loose fittings, furniture, professional fees and VAT. They do not cover any costs associated with abnormal conditions.

Running costs are for mechanical, electrical and water treatment only; they do not, for example, include maintenance or staff.

Energy costs are generally based on information from BRECSU publications (see Bibliography, page 138).

Costs are for general guidance only, as every pool will have particular characteristics which will influence both capital and operating costs. And of course costs will go up (occasionally down), in some areas more than others. But the principles and assumptions here can be applied (or varied) by people planning pools, to any particular circumstances. At the very least, it puts in a realistic perspective the relatively small contribution of water treatment and chemicals to total costs.

Buyers beware

How easy it is to store chemicals, and access to the plant, may affect the choice of disinfectant, as may the cost and availability of chemicals. The strength of chemicals can vary from brand to brand. It is important to know what strength is on offer - and that may explain price differences. The strength of supplied chemicals should be checked from time to time. The purity of disinfectant

---

SMALL CONVENTIONAL POOL
Size 20m x 8.5m
Estimated bathing load 60,000 per annum
Surface area 170m^2
Volume 200m^3
Turnover 2.5h
Circulation rate 80m^3/h

Capital costs
Water treatment (filtration, sodium hypochlorite) £80,000
Building £500,000 (550 sq m; building : water ratio 3.2 :1)
Water treatment is 16% of capital costs

Running costs per annum
Chemicals £4,000
Water £3,000
Energy £15,000
Total of chemicals, water, energy £22,000
Chemicals are 18% of running costs
Water is 14% of running costs

TEACHING POOL
Size 12m x 8m
Estimated bathing load 85,000 per annum
Surface area 96m^2
Volume 86m^3
Turnover 0.75h
Circulation rate 115m^3/h

Capital costs
Water treatment (filration, sodium hypochlorite) £85,000
Building £360,000 (400m^2; building : water ratio 4.2:1)
Water treatment is 21% of capital costs

Running costs per annum
Chemicals £3,000
Water £2,500
Energy £10,000
Total of chemicals, water, energy £15,500
Chemicals are 20% of running costs
Water is 16% of running costs

The typical pool

The choice is made. The typical pool is now fitted with the bones of a chlorine disinfection system, with filtration, dosing (disinfectant, pH correction and coagulant).
Dosing is pre-filter (see page 52)

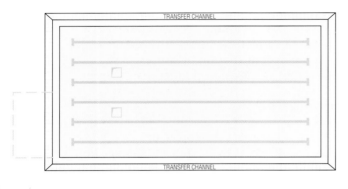

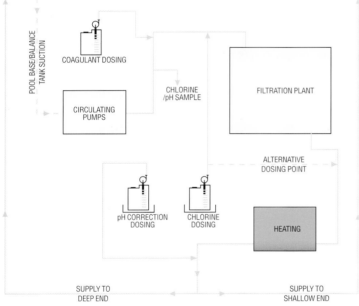

The next three chapters describe disinfectants that, by and large, could be incorporated within the principles of this basic scheme. Chapter 9 shows how to incorporate ozone and UV.

chemicals is more difficult to check. There are different grades of, for example, hypochlorites. The Committee on Chemicals and Materials of Construction for use in Public Water Supply and Swimming Pools take into account stated levels of impurity when approving disinfectants on public health grounds (see page 101). But this does not help with working out value for money.

Chapter 6

Chlorine disinfectants

This chapter is about what one might call mainstream disinfectants - those traditionally and successfully used in all sorts of indoor pool in the UK, including the most demanding. These are chlorine gas and the hypochlorites. It first describes the chemistry of chlorine disinfection, and of its byproducts. The disinfectants are then described in use - levels, pH values, etc.

Chapter 7 deals with organic disinfectants (chlorinated isocyanurates and BCDMH). These have established themselves as effective in less demanding conditions - small, lightly loaded pools, for example. Chapter 8 covers a mixed bag of disinfectants and other pool water treatments - a mixture of the relatively new or reworked and the unlikely. Chapter 9 deals separately with two systems which purify the pool water as it passes through the plant room - ozone and ultraviolet radiation.

THE CHEMISTRY OF CHLORINE DISINFECTION

An academic qualification in chemistry should not be a prerequisite for understanding and running successfully a swimming pool. But complete ignorance of what is happening within the complex solution which is the pool is a serious handicap. This section presents, as simply as possible, just the amount of pool chemistry that is relevant and helpful to pool managers and operators.

Chlorine and hypochlorites

Chlorine gas is clearly distinct from sodium and calcium hyochlorites, but their action in pool water treatment is similar enough for them all to be loosely referred to as 'chlorine'. The principal reason for adding chlorine to pool water (or the public water supply) is to destroy potentially harmful microorganisms. In reacting with the organisms the chlorine is itself destroyed, but the amount thus lost is very small compared with the amount added and compared with that used in oxidation.

Chlorine is a powerful oxidising agent and much of the polluting matter introduced to the pool water by bathers is capable of oxidation. Most of the loss of chlorine is to such oxidation; this loss must continually be made good to ensure that there is a residual level of chlorine in the pool, to deal with fresh pollution.

Chlorine gas dissolves in water and reacts reversibly (<>) with it:

$$Cl_2 + H_2O <> HOCl + HCl$$

chlorine   water   hypochlorous   hydrochloric
                      acid   acid

The hypochlorites also produce hypochlorous acid in water. There are necessarily other chemicals in the hypochlorite mixture, but the key equations are:

$$NaOCl + H_2O <> HOCl + Na^+ + OH^-$$

sodium   water   hypochlorous   sodium   hydroxide
hypochlorite   acid   ion   ion

$$Ca(OCl)_2 + 2H_2O <> 2HOCl + Ca^{++} + 2OH^-$$

calcium   water   hypochlorous   calcium   hydroxide
hypochlorite   acid   ion   ion

Hypochlorous is a weak acid and reacts further:

$$HOCl <> H^+ + OCl^-$$

hypochlorous   hydrogen   hypochlorite
acid   ion   ion

The hydrogen ion concentration is a critical parameter in pool water chemistry; from it is derived the measure of how acidic the water is - pH value. The higher the hydrogen ion concentration, the lower the pH value - ie more acidic.

The sum of hypochlorous acid and hypochlorite ion are what is measured as free residual chlorine. Because the equilibrium between the two is established almost instantaneously, chemical measurements do not distinguish between the two - although hypochlorous acid is the active disinfectant.

The effect of pH on chlorine chemistry

The position of these equilibria above is controlled by the concentrations of the compounds and ions in the reactions. Thus, in the last equation, if the hydrogen ion concentration is increased (ie pH value reduced) then the equilibrium is pushed to the left; so hypochlorous acid concentration also increases, and hypochlorite decreases. Hypochlorous acid is the stronger disinfectant of the two. So, for a given concentration of free residual chlorine, the lower the pH value the greater the disinfectant effect. Conversely, a higher pH value can severely reduce the disinfectant power - even though the free chlorine residual level is as recommended. This is why pH value should be kept relatively low, and certainly within strictly defined limits.

Many factors affect pH value, and thus disinfectant use - including the nature of the source water (see Chapter 5). Chlorine gas itself reduces pH value; sodium and calcium hypochlorites increase it; so pH values may have to corrected (see page 77).

The other factors and reactions which affect pH values cannot all be quantified, so it is impossible to maintain the correct pH value by adding a theoretical amount of alkali or acid. It is important to appreciate the way that pH value relates to other water balance parameters (see Chapter 13) - especially alkalinity (see page 78) Frequent direct measurement is necessary, using reliable testing apparatus (see Chapter 13).

Chlorine plus ammonia

Chlorine gas and the two hypochlorites react with pollutants in the water to form other products; as a result their ability to kill microorganisms is reduced. A major pollutant is ammonia (NH_3), which is continually added to pool water through the decomposition of the urea in nitrogenous products (urine, sweat, etc) introduced by bathers. The decomposition is slow, as is the subsequent reaction of ammonia with excess chlorine. The products of this reaction are chloramines, which are measured as 'combined chlorine' in standard swimming pool tests. Combined plus free chlorine is called 'total chlorine'.

The first stage of the reaction is:

$$Cl_2 + NH_3 > HCl + NH_2Cl$$
chlorine   ammonia   hydrochloric monochloramine
acid

This reaction is normal and acceptable: monochloramine is not an irritating compound; it has some disinfecting properties, but is not nearly as effective as free chlorine. Monochloramine is stable at normal pool pH values.

Given enough chlorine, however, the reaction will go further:

$$Cl_2 + NH_2Cl > HCl + NHCl_2$$
chlorine   monochloramine   hydrochloric   dichloramine
acid

Dichloramine irritates the eyes and nose, is unstable, and decomposes - provided the pool water's pH value is correct and there is enough chlorine:

$$NH_2Cl + NHCl_2 > 3HCl + N_2$$
monochloramine   dichloramine   hydrochloric   nitrogen
acid

This reaction is called breakpoint chlorination: the combined chlorine level, which will have been rising as more chlorine is added, now drops; free chlorine then rises without a corresponding rise in combined chlorine. This indicates that the pool's nitrogenous pollution has been successfully oxidised by chlorine. This should happen as long as the free chlorine level is higher - ideally, double - the combined chlorine level, and the latter less than 1mg/l. Both levels must be monitored regularly (see

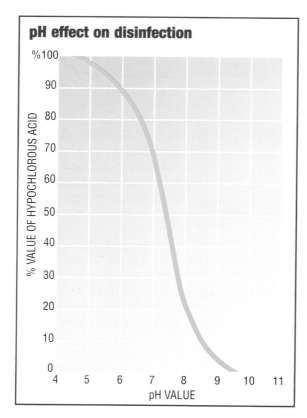

pH effect on disinfection

%100
90
80
70
60
50
40
30
20
10
0

% VALUE OF HYPOCHLOROUS ACID

4   5   6   7   8   9   10   11

pH VALUE

Chapter 13). In practice, organic chloramines (next section) complicate this, as they do not respond to breakpoint chlorination.

When things go wrong - usually because the pH value is too low and total chlorine too high - the reaction can take another course:

$$Cl_2 + NHCl_2 > HCl + NCl_3$$

chlorine   dichloramine   hydrochloric   trichloramine
                           acid   (nitrogen trichloride)

Nitrogen trichloride is the most irritant of the chloramines; together with dichloramine, it is largely responsible for the chlorine odours and eye irritation sometimes associated with chlorine-treated pools.

All these reactions are fairly slow (up to an hour in some cases) and at any one particular time of testing, there is likely to be a cocktail of the different products. The involvement of organic compounds complicate the chemistry further.

Organic chloramines As well as reacting with ammonia, chlorine reacts with organic (carbon-based) nitrogen compounds derived mainly from proteins in bather pollution. Creatinines, for example, are found in urine and sweat. The reactions are very slow - several weeks in some cases. The resulting chlorinated organic amines contribute to combined chlorine readings. But they are stable and are promoted, rather than removed, by excess chlorine. Only dilution will significantly reduce them, although pool water treated with ozone, carbon filtration or perhaps ultraviolet irradiation will reduce the amount of dilution required (see Chapter 9).

Principles A number of principles emerge from the chemistry of chlorine and ammonia. They are summarised here, but the practical detail is in Chapter 13.

- As the breakdown of urea to ammonia happens over a long period, water treatment should be continuous.
- Maintaining the correct pH value is critical.
- The less disinfectant and other chemicals needed to maintain good water, the better.
- The design bathing load set for the pool should not be exceeded.
- If pool water becomes smelly despite satisfactory chlorine residuals and pH value - and there is no obvious explanation - dilution is the best option.

THE DISINFECTANTS IN USE

This chapter has already dealt with the chemistry of chlorine disinfection. (Chapter 13 deals with pH value and water balance, and has detailed information about monitoring pool water parameters including disinfectant residual levels.) This section summarises how the disinfectants should be used. Dosing in detail is dealt with in Chapter 10.

Sodium and calcium hypochlorites

Systems using sodium or calcium hypochlorite are suitable for all types of pool.

Residual levels In order to achieve the best possible water quality, three safeguards are recommended.

- The free chlorine residual should be at the lowest level that gives satisfactory microbiological quality (see Chapter 15). This should be possible at less than 1mg/l - provided turnover, hydraulics, loading, dosing, filtration, etc are in line with the recommendations in this book. In less than these ideal conditions - quite likely with current UK practice - pools may need to exceed 1mg/l free chlorine, but the target should still be no more than 1.5-2.0mg/l.
- However good the pool, it should retain some free chlorine residual to prevent cross-infection and to cope with sudden increases in bather numbers. Although the German DIN standard specifies 0.2mg/l, here, 0.5mg/l will generally be necessary.
- The combined chlorine residual should be less than the free, ideally half or less.

Pools that do not operate to the design and other parameters in this book may need to have higher residuals - and so may have water that is less attractive, with higher combined chlorine levels. Pools that occasionally have large influxes of extra bathers need to accommodate this demand on disinfection.

pH value For hypochlorite disinfectants to work properly, the pH value of the pool water is critical. It is recommended that:

- the pH value should be maintained between 7.2 and 7.8; 7.2-7.4 should be the target, as disinfection will be more effective (as is coagulation - see page 75). The pH value can be even lower if conditions and the pool fabric allow. (The German DIN standard, for example, recommends between 6.5 and 7.6.) If, however, there is a 'chlorine' smell or irritation (ie dichloramine or trichloramine is present), the pH value may have to be raised and any bathing overload corrected, or pool dilution increased (see page 85).

Dosing with an acid is normally required with hypochlorites in order to counteract their tendency to drive up the pH value. It is recommended that:

- automatic dosing by pumps linked to a pH controller should be used if possible
- if manually controlled dosing pumps are used, they should be carefully controlled by pool operators, and monitoring of pH values should be every two hours.

In waters with a low natural alkalinity (maximum alkalinity of 150mg/l as $CaCO_3$, maximum hardness 300mg/l as $CaCO_3$) carbon dioxide is usually preferred for pH reduction. Sodium bisulphate or hydrochloric acid are alternatives - and the norm for waters with high alkalinity and hardness. Sodium bisulphate may raise the sulphate levels in the pool - see page 80.

Chlorine gas

Chlorine gas is a very effective disinfectant - the benchmark against which its replacements are measured. Given the complications that alternative sources of chlorine can bring, it is perhaps not surprising that, 20 years or so after the UK government recommended its replacement on safety grounds, a significant number of pools have not changed. Indeed, some new pools are designed for chlorine gas. In both cases, it is crucial that the installation is safe and meets all national design, operational and training guidelines.

Chapters 10, 17 and 18 give uptodate guidance on how to use chlorine gas safely. There must be prior co-operation and consultation among architects, engineers, equipment and chemical suppliers, insurance companies, pool managers and operators. Suppliers of chlorine gas should supply only to sites whose design and safety arrangements have been checked by the Health & Safety Executive (HSE), who should be consulted before finalising the design. The HSE has powers under the Health and Safety at Work, Etc Act 1974 to inspect installations to ensure that they satisfy its safety requirements. (This applies to all pools - see page 119 - but is particularly important with chlorine gas.)

Residuals, pH value These are as for hypochlorite (see page 39). Chlorine gas is acidic, so pH values will be driven down with the addition of chlorine. So a solution of sodium carbonate is normally added, by a manually or automatically controlled pump, to maintain the pH value. Alkalinity (see page 78) may need to be increased.

Electrolytic generation of hypochlorite

In the system normally used, sodium hypochlorite is generated externally to the pool by passing strong sodium chloride solution through an electrolyser. The plant must be sized, not just for the maximum load intended, but also to build up a reserve to cope with fluctuations. A standby 24-hour supply of sodium or calcium hypochlorite is also necessary to allow for maintenance work on the generator and associated equipment.

Alternatively, hypochlorite may be generated by maintaining 3,000-4,000mg/l of sodium chloride in the pool water and passing all or part of it through an electrolyser as part of the treatment process. This system is not suitable for large pools, partly because of the corrosion risk. The water will also tend to taste salty. It can be satisfactory for smaller, lightly loaded pools as long as the electrolytic generation system has sufficient flexibility and capacity to deal with variations in bathing load and therefore maintain the recommended free chlorine residual. It has to be very carefully designed. Great care should be taken to ensure that all the plant and fittings are suitable, as they are prone to corrosion. Highly explosive hydrogen gas is generated, and needs to be vented safely. These issues must be fully considered at the design stage.

Residuals, pH value Generally, electrolytically generated hypochlorite operates best at the same chlorine residuals, pH values etc as ordinary hypochlorite disinfection. As it is almost neutral, however, it should require less acid dosing. Sometimes - especially with soft acidic waters - an alkali may be needed instead.

Hypochlorite generation will give higher levels of total dissolved solids (TDS) than other chemical treatment systems; the possible effects of this on the fabric of the pool should be taken into account by pool operators.

Chapter 7

Organic disinfectants

This chapter deals with the use of two disinfectant systems that can be effective in treating pools which make less demands than busy public pools. Chloroisocyanurates and bromochlorodimethylhydantoin (BCDMH) are most commonly used in the UK for schools, hotels, clubs and holiday camps.

CHLORINATED ISOCYANURATES

The chlorinated isocyanurates are organic compounds which decompose in water to produce cyanuric acid and chlorine (and the other chlorine equilibrium products including hypochlorous acid and hypochlorite ion, as described on page 37).

Using chlorinated isocyanurates

There are two main forms of chloro-isocyanurate sold for swimming pool use in the UK - both solids - sodium dichloroisocyanurate dihydrate ('dichlor') and trichloroisocyanuric acid ('trichlor'). The methods of dosing chlorinated isocyanurates vary widely. Page 61 deals with the sort of circulation feeders that are used, but in general it is recommended that:

- for more heavily loaded and larger pools, either a dilute solution of dichlor (prepared according to the manufacturer's instructions) should be added by dosing pump; or trichlor can be dosed by a circulation feeder
- for smaller, less heavily loaded pools, trichlor tablets or sticks may be suitable, dosed by circulation feeder. Dichlor granules designed for hand dosing must be used with great care, as it is difficult to maintain the correct residual in a pool which is used continuously.

Residual levels   Chloroisocyanurates provide a reserve of free residual chlorine and so are potentially as effective as chlorine. But the more cyanuric acid there is, the more free chlorine is locked up as chloroisocyanurate. So, for the chlorine residual reserve to be

available, there must be a carefully monitored relationship between the free chlorine residual and cyanuric acid.

Cyanuric acid levels must be measured at least once a week until results are consistent, when the frequency can become monthly. Simple test kits are available (though samples have to be diluted first to measure over 80 or 100mg/l). The recommended target is:

- cyanuric acid below 200mg/l; the ideal range is 50-100mg/l.

Microbiological conditions may become unsatisfactory above 100mg/l of cyanuric acid. Regular backwashing of filters should dilute the water enough to achieve the recommended cyanuric acid concentration. If not, the fresh water dilution rate may need to be increased.

Free chlorine levels are tested using DPD reagent. In general, free chlorine residuals must be kept higher than with hypochlorite, because of the reduction in the rate of kill of bacteria with increasing concentrations of cyanuric acid. The range recommended is:

- free chlorine 2.5-5.0mg/l. The relationship between cyanuric acid and free chlorine can be tabulated:

Cyanuric acid concentration in pool (mg/l)	Minimum free chlorine (mg/l)
25	1.5
50	2.0
100	2.5
200	3.0

pH value   For effective disinfection, the pH value must be monitored. Dichlor is largely pH neutral and often needs no addition of alkali. Sometimes - with hard, alkaline waters, for example - an acid may be required instead. The pH values of pools on acid trichlor generally have to be raised - usually by dosing an alkali solution with a pump. It is recommended that:

- the pH value should be maintained between 7.2 and 7.8; the bottom of the range should be the target, as disinfection will be more effective. If, however, there is a 'chlorine' smell or irritation, the pH value may have to be raised towards the upper part of the range.

Outdoor pools
The stabilising effect of cyanuric acid on the free chlorine residual in strong sunlight makes chlorinated isocyanurates useful in outdoor pools. But the same effect can be achieved in a hypochlorite pool by adding 60mg/l cyanuric acid to the pool water at the start of the season; this should maintain the necessary minimum concentration of 25mg/l. Hypochlorite dosing must subsequently be high enough to maintain the recommended free chlorine residual for that concentration of cyanuric acid (see chart page 41).

BROMOCHLORO-DIMETHYLHYDANTOIN (BCDMH)

BCDMH dissolves in water to release both active bromine (hypobromous acid) and active chlorine (hypochlorous acid).

In chlorine systems, hypochlorous acid is the most significant disinfectant molecule, but the primary disinfectant in a pool treated with BCDMH is hypobromous acid. Like HOCl, it kills bacteria and oxidises organic matter. At the end of this process spent bromine is left in the water in the form of the bromide ion. The active chlorine (hypochlorous acid) regenerates hypobromous acid from the bromide residue.

As a result the active disinfectant in a BCDMH pool is always hypobromous acid. If hypochlorite is added to the pool, this too will reactivate the bromide residue, which can in this respect be regarded as a bromine bank.

In an equivalent way to chlorine chemistry, hypobromous acid reacts with ammonia from bather pollution to form bromamines. Monobromamine (unlike monochloramine) disinfects almost as effectively as the free bromine. So there is no need to differentiate between them in monitoring disinfectant activity. However, like chlorine, a free to combined bromine ratio of at least 2:1 is desirable, to ensure that ammonia etc are broken down. Dibromamine and tribromamine are in any case as undesirable in terms of irritation as their chlorine equivalents.

There are products which have ethylhydantoin as well as methylhydantoin: these operate in a similar way.

Using BCDMH
BCDMH is supplied as small white tablets and used in circulation feeder devices (brominators - see page 61), which may be suitable for all types of pool.

Chemical levels   Bromide is formed in pools using this system, although the concentrations found are not as high as those in pools using elemental liquid bromine. But over the years there have been reports of skin irritation and rashes after exposure to pool water treated with BCDMH (see pages 33, 91 and Bibliography, page 138). It is not clear why this should be, but it is recommended that operators are particularly vigilant about rashes.

It is specifically recommended that:
- operators should aim for a total bromine residual of between 4.0 and 6.0mg/l using DPD tests.
- the concentration of dimethylhydantoin (DMH) should not exceed 200mg/l. As there is no poolside test kit for this, monthly samples should be tested by a qualified laboratory during the first three months of BCDMH use. If 200mg/l of DMH has not been exceeded, testing can then be quarterly for nine months, and twice a year thereafter. If there is any doubt that DMH has been controlled adequately, the laboratory test should be done
- careful control of the addition of BCDMH, regular filter backwashing and a good dilution regime should keep DMH below the maximum. If not, the pool may have to be partially or completely emptied
- care is taken to watch out for high colony counts (see Chapter 15).

pH value   BCDMH is nearly neutral and has little effect on the pH values of most water supplies. Many pools treated with BCDMH require little or no pH correction. However, pH value can vary with the source of water and the conditions of the pool and for that reason it is important to measure and control pH value daily. It is recommended that:
- the pH value should be maintained between 7.2 and 7.8.

Chapter 8

Fringe treatments

This chapter deals with a variety of disinfectants and other pool water treatments that for one reason or another are outside the mainstream of pool water disinfection. Some have been around for a long time, but have proved themselves of only limited use. Others are new - or reworkings of older methods - and as yet relatively unproven.

Although PWTAG is committed to assessing their claims and their efficacy, it is not always possible to make definitive judgements. For example, reports from pools that claim success with a novel product are difficult to assess. Often the basic treatment and circulation plant may have been tuned up in preparation; it is then difficult to know what to credit with improvements in performance. That is why PWTAG prefers to rely, when it can, on results from its scale-model pool (see page 136).

PWTAG also interrogates manufacturers and distributors about the basis for their claims. Some products have been excluded from this system (and this book) because no answers have come to PWTAG's questions.

SODIUM BROMIDE PLUS HYPOCHLORITE

This system is based on well-established pool chemistry, but with a specific monitoring procedure. Sodium bromide solution and hypochlorite are dosed. A reserve of bromide is maintained in the pool water so that all the hypochlorite (sodium or calcium) dosed to the pool is converted to hypobromous acid (the disinfecting agent) and hypobromite ion. At a pH of 7.8 to 8.2, between 85 and 95% of the bromide converted becomes hypobromous acid.

A further element of the system is a solution of sodium bicarbonate and hexametaphosphate which is added to the hypochlorite day tank. This buffer minimises the production of mixed chlorbromamines.

A troublesome mixture of chloramines and bromamines can also be produced if the bromide level is too low. Howeve, irritant nitrogen trichloride is not produced.

Using sodium bromide plus hypochlorite
Sodium bromide solution is dosed - via a dosing set and timer - into the main circulation upstream from the hypochlorite dosing.

Residuals, pH, etc The *bromide* reserve is critical, and there is a specific test for this, which involves a conversion factor between chloride and bromide. The minimum is 9mg/l as bromide (4mg/l measured as chloride); some heavily used pools may need up to 15mg/l (7mg/l as chloride). This test should be carried out daily, to the manufacturer's instructions. *Total bromine* should be maintained at between 1.5 and 3.5mg/l; ideally, operators should aim for between 2.0 and 3.0mg/l. Standard DPD test kits are used for this. *pH value* should be between 7.8 and 8.2, the *total alkalinity* at least 100mg/l as $CaCO_3$.

TCDO PLUS SILICEOUS ALUMINATE

This is a relatively new system which has been approved (as usual, on safety grounds only) by the DETR Committee (page 101). A metered dose of siliceous aluminate (an anionic liquid coagulant) is continuously pumped into the pre-filtration flow. A conventional (cationic) coagulant is similarly dosed. It is claimed that the two together improve filtration and allow less frequent backwashing.

The liquid TCDO complex ($Cl_4O_{10}^-$) is dosed post-filter and reacts with free chlorine (dosed after the TCDO complex) to produce a low level of chlorine dioxide in the pool water. It is claimed that levels of chloramines, dissolved solids and trihalomethanes are minimised. TCDO complex does not react with ammonia.

Installations in pools in mainland Europe and the UK have given promising results.

METAL IONS

The generation of silver and/or copper ions has been used to disinfect small, usually domestic pools for some years; in public pools, ions alone have not been recommended, as they are not able to maintain safe bathing. More recently, ions have been used in larger pools, alongside a chlorine or bromine-based disinfectant.

Silver has a slow inhibiting effect on bacterial growth. Copper is an effective algicide, but can give considerable green-black staining problems on tiles, marbling, grout etc. (It should not exceed 1mg/l in pool water.) There are claims that ions and halogens together disinfect more effectively than the sum of their disinfectant powers - ie that there is synergy between them. There is no good evidence for this, and at present the system cannot be recommended for other than domestic pools.

There is also doubt about the microbiological test methods used to support claims for copper/silver/hypochlorite systems. Silver is not inactivated by the thiosulphate normally used when collecting water samples for microbiological analysis from halogen systems. So the silver could continue to affect bacteria in the sample. If sodium thioglycollate neutraliser is not added as well (see page 99), misleadingly reassuring coliform and plate counts may result.

POLYMERIC BIGUANIDE

This non-halogen disinfectant inactivates microorganisms but does not oxidise other bather pollution. Its efficacy as a disinfectant has not been studied independently in the UK, although some work has been done overseas. From information received, including *ad hoc* reports of its use in the UK, it is not recommended for non-domestic pools.

ZEOLITE

Clinoptolite and other zeolite materials have been marketed as a replacement for the sand in a pool filter. Claims have ranged from sparkling water to eliminating dry hair.

The significant claim that zeolite removes ammonia (especially as chloramines in the presence of chlorine) was backed up with data from analysis of samples of clinoptolite in use for some time. However, examination of the data revealed the absorption of ammonia in amounts that were trivial relative to the total amounts that would have passed through the filters in the time.

Claims about reduced backwashing were also unconvincing.

- Ten or more weeks between backwashing (a promotional quote from one user) could produce considerable microbiological contamination of the filters; also difficulties in fluidising the filter media when backwashing is done.
- The claimed savings on backwash water appear exaggerated. Any apparent savings may be negated by the need to dilute.
- The claims that ammonia is retained on the filter medium, but that regeneration of the clinoptolite has not been necessary, seem contradictory - unless the filter is nitrifying (ie bacteria are breaking down ammonia), which itself could cause problems.

PWTAG concludes that the case for zeolite is unproven.

MAGNETISM

A number of products have been marketed which incorporate magnets attached to the pool circulation pipework. The claim is that they help the pool's normal disinfection. Although some bench-scale experiments seemed to demonstrate an effect, there is no clear theoretical basis for why this should be; results on PWTAG's pilot-scale pool were inconclusive; and there is no convincing evidence that the systems work in practice.

Another product claims to soften swimming pool water and inhibit microorganisms by producing low-frequency electro-magnetic radio waves. There is no good evidence for this. The same applies to a product which makes similar claims for an electronic scale eliminator.

In summary, there is no good evidence for disinfection, conflicting evidence on scale removal and water softening, and no reason to suppose such systems could cope with large volumes.

Chapter 9

Ozone and ultraviolet

These two water treatment systems have been given a chapter of their own, to reflect the fact that they purify the pool water as it passes through the plant room. Both deal with water contaminants without producing a disinfectant residual, and allow the water in the pool itself to operate with a lower level of conventional residual disinfectant than it otherwise would. (There are relatively untried systems that combine ozone and UV on the theory that there is a synergy between them.)

OZONE

Of the two, ozone is by far the better established in the UK; it is a system that tends to be considered for most new pools which will be heavily loaded, or where particularly good quality water is wanted - especially leisure pools.

Chemistry

Ozone is a bluish gas - chemically, three oxygen atoms (O_3) as opposed to the two in the oxygen molecule (O_2). It can appear naturally around electrical equipment; for pool water disinfection, it is generated by passing a silent electric discharge through dried air. Only a small percentage of the approximately fifth of air that is oxygen is converted to ozone.

Ozone is unstable and relatively insoluble in warm water, so has to be generated and used within the treatment system. It is also toxic in significant atmospheric concentrations, so excess (unreacted) ozone must be removed by a deozonising filter within the treatment system. Its rapid reversion to oxygen makes it a very reactive oxidant, through the liberation of an oxygen atom and the formation of hydroxyl radicals; some residual molecular ozone is also available for oxidation. Ozone is pH neutral.

Dealing with contaminants etc The chemistry of the relation between ozone and pool contaminants is complex. Ozone interferes

with the reactions that produce contaminants, more than it actually destroys urea, creatinine or trihalomethanes. There are significant reactions which allow subsequent filtration of the organic molecules by a process of microflocculation. There is also a slow reaction with combined chlorine to form chloride and nitrate, thus enhancing breakpoint chlorination and the removal of ammonia. (Ozone does not react with ammonia itself.) The chemistry of ozonation indicates that the activated carbon filter is an important part of the process of ensuring that combined chlorine levels are kept low - generally below 0.2mg/l. (Activated carbon filters also remove free chlorine residual.)

Ozone is an effective virucide and bactericide.

The effect, then, of ozonation, microflocculation and filtration is to enhance the purity of the water before it re-enters the pool. As a result, the low level of chlorine added to the water after filtration is nearly all available as a free chlorine residual for the pool. Well-managed ozone pools are generally odour-free.

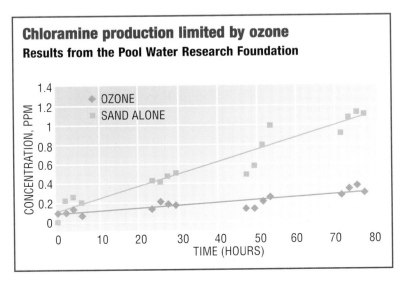

Chloramine production limited by ozone
Results from the Pool Water Research Foundation

Feed gas preparation

The air for ozonation is dried and filtered to remove dust and to achieve a dewpoint of, typically, minus 60°C. The driers must be fed with air within a range (specified by the manufacturer) of temperature and humidity - if necessary by pretreatment. The air output quality should be monitored by a dewpoint meter or by a thermocouple on the drier outlet connected via a microprocessor.

Ozone generation

Ozone is generated by a corona or silent electrical discharge produced by a high AC voltage (typically around 12,000 volts) through an air gap between a high voltage electrode and a glass dielectric. The discharge changes some oxygen in the air to ozone - at least 20 and typically up to 30g/m^3. The generation of ozone is influenced by the:

- volume of gas used (which also affects the concentration)
- voltage and frequency
- temperature of the cooling water
- dewpoint of the air.

Heat is produced during the discharge and generators for pools are normally water cooled (smaller ones may be air cooled). Thus glass, water, air and high-voltage electricity are in close proximity. Generators must therefore be of proven design, well understood by operators and maintained to manufacturers' instructions.

Air from the driers is drawn through the generator under a vacuum to remove the chance of a dangerous escape of ozone. The quantity of ozone generated is controlled (automatically or manually) by adjusting the voltage. The efficiency should be around 20 watts per gram of ozone.

Ozone contact system

The ozone must be mixed with the whole body of water, because of its low solubility. Also ozone must transfer from the gaseous to the liquid phase. So mixer design is critical, as is ozone concentration. The maximum solubility of ozone is about 3mg/l at 30°C, and difficult to achieve.

In pools the system normally comprises a booster pump forcing pool water through an injector, which draws in the air/ozone from the generator into a mixer. Here the intimate mixing of fine bubbles with the water is effected. The ozone transfer is about 90%.

Following mixing, the ozone residual must be in contact with the water for at least 2 minutes, preferably longer, to give as much reaction as possible between the ozone and polluting material. The air and undissolved ozone is released from the water and passed through an ozone removal system before it can be discharged to the atmosphere. Failure to remove all entrained air can lead to subsequent release of air in the pool, with loss of clarity; this is an important part of the process.

Safety

Ozone is a toxic gas with a half life in cold dry air of 30-40 minutes - more stable than in

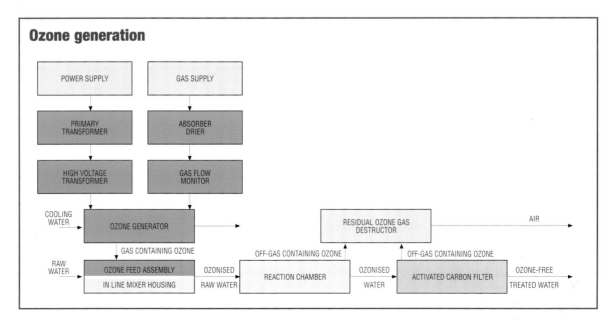

water. Concentrations of 10mg/m^3 in air lead to serious irritation and breathing difficulties. The threshold limiting value is 0.2mg/m^3. Although ozone has a distinctive smell (characteristic of old-fashioned photocopiers) the nose is not a reliable guide for this. So it is important that the ozone generation system fails safe and gives adequate warning on failure.

Generators which are controlled through microprocessors are more reliable. Optimum operating safety is achieved by continuous attention to ten issues:

- cooling water temperature
- high-tension transformer temperature
- air feed quality
- loss of vacuum
- door protection switch
- air flow
- current flow to regenerator, booster pump and high-voltage transformer
- battery failure in the programmable logic controller
- voltage/current relationship
- interlock with water flow being treated.

These should all be connected to an alarm in the event of failure. It is also necessary to ensure the location of the ozone system is a safe environment:

- an emergency shut-down switch, clearly labelled, near the door of the room
- good ventilation
- closed, lockable room
- not a permanent place of work
- restricted access sign.

Ozone leak detectors are strongly recommended for positive pressure ozonation systems.

Installation, commissioning, maintenance

As ozonators incorporate high-tension transformers and produce a toxic gas, it is essential that service and commissioning is done by a qualified expert. They will have had specialist training, relevant experience, and be familiar with the regulations for protection and prevention of accidents. They must be in a position to judge the working conditions and confirm their safety. The manufacturer should provide the training and supply comprehensive instruction manuals. Daily records should be kept to ensure that the system is working correctly.

The typical pool

The typical pool (as it was in Chapter 5) is now fitted with ozone treatment, in accordance with the guidelines in this chapter.

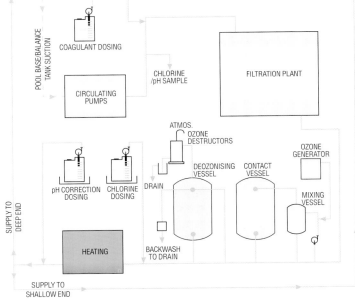

Next, the UV possibility - page 50

Dosing with ozone

There are two different ways in which ozone can be used.

- On new installations, all the water to the pool should be dosed with O_3 at a concentration that depends on the specific system being used. The British Water/PWTAG Code of Practice (see Bibliography) details the different recommended systems. Ozone acts best in contact with filtered water, so systems with separate filtration, ozonation and deozonation are best; cheaper all-in-one systems are a compromise.

- On existing installations where, due to space restrictions, it is not possible to install equipment to ozonate the total flow rate of the system, treatment of a percentage of this flow rate may be considered. This so-called slipstream ozonation should dose a minimum of 20% of the flow rate. The benefits of slipstream ozonation in dealing with contaminants will be proportional to the percentage of water ozonated; but installation costs will not be, so cost-effective benefits are likely to be difficult to achieve. Virucidal and bactericidal activity may not even be proportional.

In each case the contact time between ozone and water should be at least 2 minutes; and the concentration during this period 0.8-$1mgO_3$/l. This is a minimum: 3 minutes is better; and if the pool water temperature is over 32°C, the concentration should be 1.2-$1.5mgO_3$/l.

Deozonation

The deozonising stage immediately follows ozonation; all traces of toxic ozone must be removed from the treated water before it enters the pool. There are two common media used for deozonation:

- granular activated carbon (GAC) with a microporous surface of at least $1,000m^2$/g, and a bed depth of about 0.5m
- unactivated heat-treated anthracite or coal which has a lower adsorbent surface area of less than $500m^2$/g, and a bed depth of about 0.7m.

Carbon filtration in general is dealt with on page 73. Ozone systems may incorporate ozone monitors before and after the carbon filter. With the system that combines ozone and ultraviolet, the UV will remove residual O_3.

Bacterial colonisation Chlorine is removed with the ozone. If it is totally removed, bacterial colonisation of the filter may result. So it is important to maintain some degree of residual disinfection throughout deozonation if possible. And vigorous backwashing to break up colonies of, especially, *Pseudomonas aeruginosa*, is important. Recent experience has indicated that colonisation is likely in the deozonation media (particularly GAC) if the bed depth exceeds the levels recommended above, or if the velocity through the media is too low. Velocities between 33 and 37m/h work successfully in a deozonation plant.

Residual dosing

After ozonation and deozonation, the water should be essentially free from microorganisms, and most of the organic matter oxidised. It does not, however, contain enough residual disinfectant to prevent cross-infection within the pool itself and a disinfectant residual must be provided, normally chlorine-based. The chlorine system must be designed as if it is the main disinfection process, to provide backup should the ozonation fail.

The free chlorine residual should be substantially lower than with chlorine alone - as low, again, as will still give satisfactory microbiological monitoring results. Around 0.5mg/l should be possible - although much will depend on the turnover rate, pool hydraulics, bathing load and the consistency with which the disinfectant residual can be maintained. With slipstream ozonation, free chlorine residuals will have to be higher - more like those with chlorine alone (see page 39).

pH value

In all cases the pH value should be maintained between 7.2 and 7.8; operators should aim for the bottom of this range. The agent for pH control should be selected according to the nature of the disinfectant.

Publications

In 1986 PWTAG published *Ozone Water Treatment Systems for Swimming Pools: A national survey* (now out of print; inquiries to PWTAG Secretary - see page 137). British Water and PWTAG publish the *Code of Practice for Ozone Plant for Swimming Pool Water* (see Bibliography).

ULTRAVIOLET RADIATION

The disinfectant ability of radiation from the ultraviolet (UV) section of the electromagnetic spectrum is well established. UV is often used in drinking water, industrial and effluent applications to kill bacteria. Its ability to affect other chemical bonds has been exploited to remove trace organics from purified water, break down pesticides in drinking water, etc.

In swimming pools, UV has more recently been used to disinfect and assist in the breakdown of chloramines and other organic pollutants by photo-oxidation. There, it is essential to maintain a persistent disinfectant residual throughout the system. Lower residual chlorine levels than the same pool without UV should be adequate; though potential disinfectant cost savings are offset somewhat by the cost of the chlorine consumed in the photo-oxidation process.

Other benefits are claimed, but although there are dozens of UV installations in swimming pools, clear evidence of their effectiveness is less plentiful.

The mechanism
PWTAG research at Cranfield University in 1997, using low-pressure UV lamps, confirmed that the chlorine-nitrogen and hydrogen-nitrogen bonds in chloramines are vulnerable to photo-oxidation by UV. Chloramines were measurably reduced. On the other hand, the research also found a small increase in halogenated organics such as chloroform and other trihalomethanes.

The system
A typical UV unit consists of one or more UV lamps in a treatment chamber made from a grade of stainless steel chosen to stand up to the water treatment. The system is installed in the full circulation pipework of the pool, so that the pool water is treated on a regular, continuous basis. As with ozone, treatment of only part of the pool circulation brings at best proportional benefits.

The UV lamps are protected from the water by a quartz glass sleeve. Contaminants must be regularly removed from the sleeves - normally by an automatic system, though manual cleaning is sometimes practicable in a lightly used pool. The quartz glass has been known to break, so a 250 micron in-line strainer is

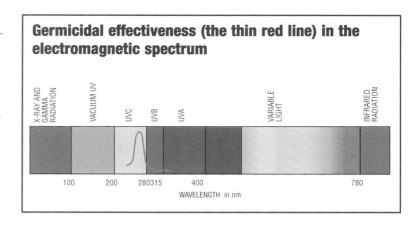

Germicidal effectiveness (the thin red line) in the electromagnetic spectrum

X-RAY AND GAMMA RADIATION | VACUUM UV | UVC | UVB | UVA | VARIABLE LIGHT | INFRARED RADIATION

100   200   280 315   400   780

WAVELENGTH in nm

recommended to prevent glass fragments entering the pool. The friction loss of this must be added to that in the UV unit itself, in calculating the increase necessary in the generating head of the circulating pump.

A UV monitor on the chamber's outer wall should warn if the dose transmitted through the water falls below the prescribed level for any reason. Multi-lamp chambers will normally have individual lamp-failure warnings, linked to alarms if necessary. Chambers' inlets and outlets should have sampling points.

UV lamps must not be operated outside their enclosures, as UV can damage eyes and skin. Medium-pressure UV lamps require high-tension power supplies.

Lamp types   UV lamps for swimming pools are either low or medium pressure. This refers to the pressure of the mercury vapour in them. All UV lamps degrade with time: it is important to establish that all performance claims relate to the output of the lamp at the end of its working life.

Low-pressure lamps have an output of typically 60-120 watts. The number required will depend on the volume of water treated. They have a useful life of about 8,000 hours and convert around 30% of the input energy to mainly short wavelength (254nm) bactericidal UV. Their output is affected by temperature, and if the water treated is above 25°C, further allowance must be made when sizing the system.

Medium-pressure lamps have outputs up to 7 kilowatts, and so are usually used singly. They have a useful life of about 4,000 hours and an efficiency of under 15% . Their UV output

The typical pool

The typical pool is now fitted with UV treatment, in accordance with the guidelines in this chapter.

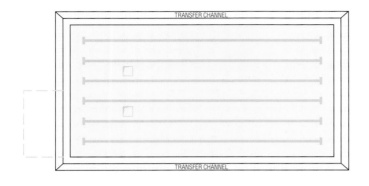

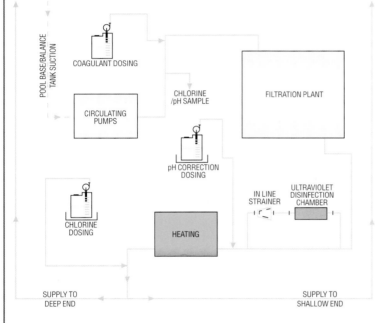

The pool now rests for a chapter, while dosing is considered; its water circulation is completed in Chapter 11.

covers a broader spectral band (from shortwave UV to visible) than low-pressure lamps. Medium-pressure lamps were the first to be used for pools; low-pressure are also now used.

Sizing

UV systems should be sized so that the dose reflects the product of UV intensity and the time of exposure. The minimum dose should be $60mJ/cm^2$, based on the actual circulation flow. This should deal with a pool whose turnover is about 3 hours; if it is significantly more or less than that, the manufacturer's advice should be sought about sizing and dosing. The UV system's sizing should also take into account results of analysis of the pool water's ability to transmit UV light.

Chapter 10

Dosing

Pool chemicals are generally dosed as solutions, either diluted from the solution supplied, or as a slurry or solution prepared from solid materials or gases. So this chapter deals with how soluions are dosed - principle and practice, dilution and dissolving, dosing strength and sizes. It covers the equipment - day tanks, pumps, pipes, valves, etc - and their operation. It finishes with two contrasting sections - automatic control and circulation feeders.

Whatever the dosing system, it is important that all equipment is operated and maintained by personnel trained by the manufacturers or an accordance with their written instructions. (There is advice on maintaining dosing equipment in Chapter 21.)

DOSING PRINCIPLES

Any particular dosing requirements of the different disinfectant and other chemicals are dealt with in Chapters 6 to 9. But there are certain important principles.

- Automatic dosing is best: electronic sensors monitor pH value and residual disinfectant levels continuously and adjust the dosing correspondingly to maintain correct levels. But regular verification of the system (including manual tests on pool water samples), and good management of it, are important. See page 84 for details.
- Manual systems, too, must be backed up by good management of operation and monitoring.
- Trying to compensate for inadequacies in treatment by shock dosing is bad practice - and can generate extra unwelcome byproducts (see page 95).
- Dosing pumps should be designed to shut themselves off if the circulation system fails (though automatic water quality monitors should remain in operation).
- Disinfectants are, on balance, best dosed before the filters in the circulation system, to avoid the inadvertent mixing of acids

and disinfectant, and to reduce bacterial colonisation of the filters. But see page 52 for a fuller account of the issue.
- pH adjusting chemicals are best dosed downstream from the filters - where possible, after the heat exchanger.
- It is important that disinfectants and pH value adjusting chemicals are well mixed with the water at the point of dosing.
- Hand dosing (ie putting chemicals directly into the pool) is rarely justified. (Dichloroisocyanurate - see page 41 - can be an exception.) It is important that all relevant health and safety issues have been settled first, and that the pool is empty of bathers until the chemical has dispersed.
- Dosing systems, like circulation, should continue 24 hours a day in order to maintain stable conditions for bathers.
- Alkaline chemicals can block injection fittings, particularly with hard water; regular cleaning may be necessary.

Component design

When it comes to considering the design of the components of a dosing system, there is a further set of principles to be honoured.
- Where appropriate, day tanks should be used to reduce the chance of major accident through over-dosing. Day tanks reduce the amount of chemical that can be incorrectly dosed into the system should there be a failure. They should be bunded (ie walled round so spillages are contained).
- As different chemicals are basically incompatible, the dosing systems as well as the tanks should be kept separate and bunded separately. There must be separate pumps for transferring each chemical.
- All systems should be fail safe: ie no fault should create dangerous conditions.
- All chemical pipework, suction and delivery lines and tanks should be marked to meet regulations and to identify the exact contents. Pipes should be labelled with the direction of flow as well as coded for their contents.

- Ideally, pipes and their connections should have different fittings for different chemicals. At the very least, they should be installed so that cross connections are impossible.
- All systems should be installed and identified so that written work procedures can be followed safely.
- Suction lines, dosing pumps, delivery lines and injection points should be as close as possible to the flow and return pipework, to avoid extended systems - but without obstructing routine access.
- Pipe runs should be as short as possible.
- Dosing systems should be accessible only to authorised personnel, and not be in a general working area.
- All materials should be corrosion-resistant - externally as well as internally - and able to withstand the pressure in the system.
- Pipe runs containing aggressive chemicals should be double contained where leakage could cause damage to people or plant.

DOSING PRACTICE

This section deals with the mechanics of dosing disinfectants and pH chemicals. Coagulant dosing is dealt with in Chapter 12 (page 75).

Before or after filter?

There is some controversy about whether to dose disinfectants before or after the filter. (Acids and alkalis are always best dosed post-filter.) With some systems, however, there is no doubt. Gas chlorinators and other dosing systems which are operated by water from the delivery of the circulation pump must dose back before the pump and therefore pre-filter. Ozone, UV, and carbon filtration demand post-filter disinfectant dosing.

Elsewhere, either is possible. There are two arguments in favour of pre-filter dosing of disinfectant.
- On traditional safety grounds, keeping disinfection separated (by the filter) from acid dosing is better. In the event of a failure of both circulation pump and flow sensor, continued disinfectant dosing will not mix with acid and produce chlorine gas which may get to the pool. This is a significant cause of serious accidents. The Health & Safety Executive endorse this approach. On the other hand, some

operators may be able, after a full risk assessment, to be confident about a system of fail safe devices and personnel training to support post-filter disinfectant dosing.
- Pre-filter dosing ensures that the filter itself gets the highest possible dose of disinfectant, which will help minimise growth in the filter media of microorganisms such as *Pseudomonas aeruginosa*. On the other hand, even with post-filter dosing, there should be enough free chlorine in the return from a well-run pool to do the job, given good filters and good backwashing.

There are also arguments in favour of post-filter dosing.
- The less disinfectant passing through the filter, the less reaction there will be with organic material, which can produce chloramines and trihalomethanes (both potentially harmful - see page 94). But there will always be some disinfectant there, contributing to what is in any case a rather inexact science.
- Sodium hypochlorite and other alkaline disinfectants can increase pH value slightly, sometimes beyond the range (6.5-7.2) at which aluminium coagulants operate best. If a pool is operating above that range anyway, this argument does not apply.

Putting safety first, PWTAG believes that pre-filter disinfectant dosing is generally the better option, but pool managers who wisely sum up the pros and cons in their particular case can make their own decision. pH adjusting chemicals are best dosed, where possible, after the heat exchanger. In each case, it is important that the chemicals mix well with water at the point of dosing.

Injection fittings

These connect the chemical delivery line to the pool water circulation pipework. Dosing points should be:
- below head height and easily accessible for maintenance
- at least ten pipe diameters from any other dosing or sampling point
- located where any slight leakage from one does not drip on to a lower one, or any other critical component, causing corrosion and subsequent failure.

Blockage of the sodium or calcium hypochlorite injection points can be minimised by the addition of sodium hexametaphosphate to the dosing tank. Injection fittings for alkalis - including hypochlorites - should be withdrawable, so that they can be descaled. All injection fittings should incorporate a non-return valve to prevent pool water from entering the chemical dosing system - particularly when the plant is shut down. Injection points can be fitted with an assembly which enables the operator to rod through them to clear blockages.

DILUTING SODIUM HYPOCHLORITE AND HYDROCHLORIC ACID

Although dilution may be necessary, it is worth considering dosage directly from the containers. In this case, smaller volumes need to be pumped; special suction assemblies are then necessary to fit to the neck of the container. The sludge produced by diluting sodium hypochlorite with hard water can be avoided by using special grades of hypochlorite.

Dilution should be by transfer of a known quantity of concentrate to the tank either by manual or electric transfer pump, topping up with water and mixing thoroughly. Alternatively, a plumbed-in device can be used to transfer the liquid concentrate into dilution water. This is less suitable for sodium hypochlorite as the eductor may scale up.

With hydrochloric acid, the concentrate is typically drawn into a water-operated venturi or injector which discharges into the day tank. Such dilutions are not highly accurate, but at least strong acid does not have to be handled. The acid actively fumes, so an open container is a hazard even without spillage. Indeed, whenever fuming acid is held in a day tank or other container, there must be special provision (good seals, etc) to prevent the fumes escaping into the atmosphere. Fumes are a threat to the fabric of the building as well as health.

DISSOLVING DRY CHEMICALS

There are several dry feeding systems which automatically prepare solutions from dry chemicals. The powder (often called granules) may be transferred to a hopper and then fed, perhaps by means of a volumetric screw, into a stirred tank of water. From there the prepared solution is pumped to the point of use. Alternatively, the dry material may be extracted from the drum and carried to the tank. In either case, the system must be engineered so as to prevent the powder getting damp, which causes caking and blockages, or even (as with dichlorocyanurates and calcium hypochlorite) a hazard.

Calcium hypochlorite granules can be fed direct from 40 or 45kg drums. Such dry feeders can incorporate an auger, a hopper drum inverter or a suction pipe to transport the granules via a dissolving mechanism into the water circulation. It is vital that no oil is able to mix with the hypochlorite, as a spontaneous explosion can result.

The quantity of dry powder used must be large enough to justify such equipment. And operators should check on the success of similar installations before going ahead. If the system has to be stripped down to clear blockages, more hazards may be introduced.

For many pools it may be satisfactory for the specified quantity to be added manually to a tank of water and stirred until dissolved. Sodium carbonate and bicarbonate are commonly made up as 5% solutions (5kg of powder or ganules in 100 litres of water) - though they may throw out a deposit in hard water. Calcium hypochlorite is best made up as a dilute mix of up to 3% (3kg in 100 litres). Calcium hypochlorite does not dissolve completely, though, so the tank is best kept stirred and a weak solution moved on to the point of application by a relatively large pump operating at a high stroke rate. Nevertheless, sludge will be deposited in the tank, which will need periodic clearing out.

DOSE STRENGTH AND DOSING UNIT SIZE

It is important when sizing disinfection equipment that the dose rate is based on the pool capacity, circulation rate and maximum bathing load which together will allow the dosing unit to be accurately sized. Operators must know how to calculate the dosing solution strength, and understand how this will vary with different types of chemical.

If the dosing equipment is undersized, the desired disinfection level will not be achieved.

If the equipment is oversized, the pool will be tend to be under or over-dosed - depending on the efficiency of the distribution and automatic control sampling systems - and more difficult to control.

So, to maintain a stable disinfectant level, it is vital to combine efficient distribution and automatic control systems with correctly sized dosing pumps and disinfectant of known solution strength.

Solution strength
There is considerable variance between sodium and calcium hypochlorite in terms of dosing pump sizing.
- Sodium hypochlorite would normally be dosed in its undiluted delivery concentration; the strength would be about 10% as available chlorine.
- Calcium hypochlorite is supplied in tablet or granular form at about 68% by weight of available chlorine. The granules are then mixed to a solution strength of no more than 3% solution (3kg solid in 100 litres of water), as this minimises blockage of solution lines and injectors.

So the dosing pump for calcium hypochlorite should have a capacity three to ten times greater than that for sodium; and the difference in volume of solution pumped would also affect the size of the solution line.

Dosing systems
The best way of achieving stable disinfectant dosing is using a pre-mixed solution of known strength and a positive displacement pump (see page 55). An alternative is a circulation feeder (see page 61).

On most feeder systems, the water supply to the feeder is taken from the pressure side of the main circulating pumps and returns to the suction side of the pumps - creating a differential pressure through the feeder unit. This has the advantage that it fails safe if water circulation stops. The pressure varies with the hydraulic conditions at each installation, the setting of the control valves on the circulation system, the cleanliness of the sand filter, etc.

Feeder system efficiency can be improved by installing a separate small pumping unit on the supply line to the feeder, with a flow meter which allows the flow rate to be pre-set. The operating water supply can then be drawn and returned from the same area on the filtration circulating system, thus stabilising factors affecting the flow rate to the feeder. A fail safe device will be needed.

DAY TANKS

Day tanks should be built of UV-stabilised polyethylene, although fabricated polypropylene tanks are suitable for chemicals other than hypochlorites. They should have:
- level indicator alarms at high level (overflow), low level (refilling) and extra-low level (alarm and close down), or clearly visible means of determining the tank contents
- overflow (to bund)
- connection to bulk tank (if there is one), including inlet valves
- water inlet (dilution, mixing) from head tank or pool (water byelaws do not allow direct connection; it must be a break connection)
- suction pipework to pump, away from the bottom of the tank. This pipework should include a strainer except where insoluble residues of calcium hypochlorite or carbon slurries are being dosed

Bulk and day tanks for sodium hypochlorite

- a drain for removal of solids and sludge from the bottom of the tank; or be easily disconnected to pick up and wash out.

It may also need to have:
- a liquid dilution device
- a liquid chemical transfer pump from the container the chemical comes in; if there is more than one day tank, each should have its own pump
- an electric stirrer for preparing solutions.

Day tanks normally have fixtures on the top to mount dosing pumps: this keeps suction lines relatively short, and avoids the possibility of syphoning. This could happen if the head of liquid on the suction side of the pump exceeds the pressure on the delivery side and all valves in the system fail.

DOSING PUMPS

The first issue to be resolved in the choice of dosing pump is capacity; pump type and construction is also dealt with in this section.

Capacity

Choosing a dosing pump's capacity is not easy with swimming pool chemicals (except for coagulants, which are pumped at the rates which depend simply on pool water volume - see page 75). All other chemicals must be pumped at rates which depend more on bathing load and water characteristics. Dosing for pH control is the most difficult of all to size.

Nevertheless, pumped dosing systems are extremely flexible; experience allows some basic rules of thumb. For example, the traditional maximum rating for a pump to dose 10% sodium hypochlorite (as available chlorine) is 5mg/l of chlorine dosed as Cl_2, or 50 ml/m^3 of recirculated water. This would nowadays be considered appropriate for a leisure pool (or an outdoor pool); a conventional pool might be rated 2.5mg/l, and a diving pool 2mg/l. The corresponding ratings for other chlorine-based disinfectants can be calculated based on the percentage of available chlorine in the solution.

Although capacity should be matched to peak loading conditions, it is not necessary to size it up to allow for shock dosing. This can compromise the accuracy of dosing at normal rates - and shock dosing is in any case not generally recommended.

The pump should be capable of delivering the required amount at the maximum back pressure of the system, including that imposed by filters, pipework, valves, bends and the pressure in the pool water circulation pipe, which is greatest before filter backwashing.

Acid dosing   Although much less acid is dosed than disinfectant - sometimes none - acid dosing pumps are often the same size as sodium hypochlorite pumps. This simplifies maintenance (as spares common to both types of pump can be stocked), and their in-built flexibility should allow correct dosing rates. With soft water (where the demand for acid is related simply to the amount of disinfectant dosed) smaller pumps can sensibly be used, or more dilute chemicals pumped. Generally, the amount of acid used depends on the amount of hypochlorite used.

Pump type and construction

Positive displacement diaphragm pumps are the norm for feeding solutions in pool water treatment. Peristaltic pumps are used on some small installations. Piston pumps are not used. Pumps must comply with current regulations and directives - and new ones should carry the CE mark.

Diaphragm pumps operate by the reciprocating action of a diaphragm forcing liquid through a delivery valve on its forward stroke and drawing it into the liquid end of the pump on its suction or backward stroke. The motive force is either an electric motor or a solenoid.

The design of pumps, and of the chemical dosing system as a whole, should incorporate features that ensure:
- the safe decompression and/or flushing of parts containing chemical solutions
- safe priming on start up
- the safe dispersal of gases formed by the natural decomposition of pool chemicals
- safe pressure relief in the event of a blocked pipe or injection fitting
- that siphoning is prevented.

The materials of the liquid ends of pumps should withstand the chemical corrosion and physical pressures. The outside of the pump and associated fittings should also withstand chemical corrosion and be rated to spillage protection class IP65.

Where there are insoluble residues of calcium hypochlorite or slurries of carbon, the stroking rate should be kept high (100+ strokes per minute), and the velocity in the pipework high; and flushing systems built in. Oversizing pump power and valves sizes can be good practice. If a pool is changing from sodium to calcium hypochlorite, pumps must be checked - and probably changed, as pumps installed for the former are almost always too small and may be the wrong construction for the latter. This is because calcium hypochlorite solutions should be dosed at a solution strength of up to 3% (expressed as available Cl_2) and down to 0.5% if possible (whereas sodium hypochlorite is usually pumped at 10-15%).

PIPEWORK

In general, all pipework must be made from materials resistant to the chemicals being conveyed at the system temperature and pressure, and identified. They should be supplied or recommended by the pump manufacturer. When working out the maximum pressure the system may have to take if all safeguards fail, calculations must assume that the dosing pump is working at its maximum pressure against a blockage. To prevent the danger of bits flying off with explosive force, either pumps must be unable to produce enough pressure to do this, or there must be a system of pressure relief. Pipes are normally plastic to ensure chemical resistance.

Pipework passing across working areas should be protected against physical damage. Where a fracture could cause damage to people or property (particularly if overhead), the delivery pipe can be run through a protective sleeve or pipe. The protective pipes should be freely draining and arranged so that any leakage gets back to that chemical's bunded area - or another safe collection point. Pipes should run as directly as possible between points, without cross connection. Right-angle bends should be avoided (as they may get brittle and crack there) and flexible tubing or swept bends used where possible.

Pipework must be sized according to the flow of chemical through it; sizes should not be mixed. It should run separately for each

chemical system, and installed so that interchange is not possible during maintenance. Changes between sodium and calcium hypochlorite will often mean changing pipework size.

VALVES AND FITTINGS

Isolating valves should be installed wherever items may need to be removed from the system, as well as for operational reasons. They should be ball rather than diaphragm valves. Special valves in the delivery line are usually required to relieve excess pressures generated by the dosing systems if valves are wrongly closed, or blocked. This is normally done with pressure-relief valves set safely above the system pressure. (The avenue for relief of pressure must be carefully chosen.) Alternatively, pumps may have a limiter, or stall at a safe pressure (but this pressure should be verified and the system tested accordingly). Motor driven pumps can generate very high system pressures, causing something to fail - perhaps dangerously.

Pressure relief valves should be located close to the pump, and should lead liquid back into the day tanks - preferably with a signal that this is happening. Calcium hypochlorite can settle and block a valve (and even, dangerously, a line); this must be taken into account when siting relief valves.

Back pressure valves normally operate at positive pressure in the delivery line, close to the pump. They may be needed for dosing accuracy where system pressures are low or vary. This would happen if dosing has to be before the pool water recirculating pump (not recommended for liquid chemicals).

A priming valve, or some other means of relieving pressure before breaking joints for maintenance, is essential.

OPERATION

Written procedures are essential for day tank filling, mixing or diluting chemicals and cleaning injectors, etc. There must also be built-in safeguards to cover those periods when the plant is not attended. Operational procedures should include a general survey to make sure the whole system is operating satisfactorily.

Calibration

Volumetric calibration of the dosing pumps is not normally necessary after it is done at commissioning. Accurate calibration is not relevant because of variation in the solution strength - due to coarse methods of preparation or chemical instability. What matters is the stability provided by feedback control via pH and chlorine residual analysers, and confirmation by water testing. But it is worth checking from time to time that pumps are still operating at the correct stroke rate and that liquid is being pumped through the injection lines.

Faults

The system must fail safe if a fault develops: the system shuts down and an alarm sounds. There is little danger in turning off the treatment system for a short period to investigate a problem, as long as there are adequate reserves of disinfectant in the pool water.

Any disruption to the pool circulation must interrupt chemical treatment to prevent chemical build up in the system - which could gas pool users when circulation restarts. (With halogen-based disinfectants the gas is chlorine, formed by the combination of disinfectant and acid dosed into the water confined in the pipe.)

If the dosing plant is water operated (eg circulation feeders - see page 61), the water should come from the pool system and it too would fail safe with the circulation failure. Equally, dosing pumps regulated by a water flow meter signal offer a simple fail safe system. Otherwise there must be at least an electrical interconnection between the main recirculation pumps, motor starters and the dosing pumps so that the dosing stops on motor failure. But this is best supplemented by pressure or flow sensors (which themselves fail safe), closing the system down when the main water system loses pressure or flow. This will overcome problems of loss of main circulation pump prime, even when the motor runs. An additional sample point may be installed to feed, say, a residual chlorine monitor, purely as an alarm if the chlorine residual gets too high - to indicate overdosing through circulation pump failure, for example. This is suggested in *Managing Health & Safety in Swimming Pools* (see Bibliography).

During shut-down periods of more than a few days, valves in filling lines between the day and bulk tanks should not be closed, as decomposition products from trapped hypochlorite may build up pressure. After such a shut down, the whole of the dosing system should be flushed through gently with low-pressure water.

COMMISSIONING

Commissioning should be done by trained and experienced engineers from the manufacturer or contractor. Electrical tests must be conducted so that the system can be commissioned to Institute of Electrical Engineers (IEE) regulations. The commissioning details should be set down, and added to the written instructions in the manuals. The whole system should first be tested with water, ensuring that:

- there are no leaks under test pressure
- relief valves do relieve at the correct pressure and in the correct direction
- pumps are calibrated
- pressure peaks do not exceed the maximum specified operating pressure
- all parts are secure and there is no vibration
- suction and delivery pipework is securely fixed, with no mechanical stress to fixed parts (eg pump discharge is best connected to rigid delivery pipe by means of flexible pipe).

The system can then be commissioned running with chemicals, looking at the same points until tests indicate satisfactory performance.

AUTOMATIC CONTROL

The chemical treatment of pool water is best automated for both disinfectant and pH control. Such controllers will optimise chemical treatment in the face of variations in bathing load, pool activity, even sunshine on the pool. Automatic systems do not, however, replace human operators (though they may give an alarm when a manual chore, like filling a tank, has been missed). And they do require proper calibration when first set up and regularly thereafter. In particular, the choice of sample points is critical (see this page): poor sampling may result in worse water treatment than manual dosing.

Automatic control is based on set points. These are the levels of disinfectant residual and pH value that are appropriate for the pool. The controllers must be programmed with this information, so that they operate to maintain the set points. In order to get the right set-up, Chapter 13 should also be consulted.

A knowledge of the basics of closed loop control is essential.

Closed loop control

Closed loop control relies on analysis of a representative sample of pool water, followed by the automatic adjustment of the dosing system to maintain the level at a point previously set. The analyser detects any error and a dosing correction is applied. As bathing load and water use changes, the quantity of chemical required varies and the system

adjusts to that. The control systems may also have to cope with a wide range of pool types from spa to leisure, with intermittent features like aeration and wave machines.

In order to deal with all this, automatic systems must take into acccount the different elements that affect closed loop control - mixing, contact time, sampling and calibration.

Mixing

To ensure a representative sample of pool water for analysis, the dosed chemical must be thoroughly mixed before sampling. In a closed pipe, mixing will not be instantaneous, however good the injection fitting. Generally an energy input of some sort is necessary, and this would be measured as head loss. This can be achieved by dosing before bends, tees or orifice plate; or by relying on the movement of flow through a length of pipe some five or six times its diameter.

In any case mixing must be complete before the water enters the pool or the next treatment phase.

Contact time

It will take some time for the dosed chemical to disperse more or less completely in the water or for the reaction with water to be complete. On a flow-through system this is significant. But on a recirculation system like a swimming pool, this is largely immaterial as the automatic control will be set to achieve pH and disinfectant levels that provide safe and pleasant bathing. Of more importance is getting a representative sample.

Sampling

The sample for automatic analysis must be representative of pool conditions, so that the control system can register what it is achieving. But chlorine residual, say, will vary across the pool - depending on bathing load, residence time due to circulation hydraulics, etc. So it may be necessary to compromise by having a set point which is different from the ideal in order to achieve satisfactory conditions everywhere in the pool. Such compromises are minimised - and sampling and control is best - in well designed pools with short turnover periods and good circulation patterns.

Good pool conditions may be achieved by sampling:

How closed loop control works

WATER FLOW →

DOSING POINT

7.22pH

SAMPLE

pH CONTROLLER

pH SENSOR

ACID DOSING SET

THE RATE AT WHICH THE CHEMICAL DOSING PUMP ADDS ACID DEPENDS ON THE DEVIATION OF THE SAMPLE VALUE FROM THE SET POINT OF THE CONTROLLER

- on the pool return to the plant room if the pool has good mixing and circulation and a rapid turnover
- from the pool itself if turnover is slow - eg one-third of the way along the pool, 300mm below the surface. (The safety of the outlet fittings should be established, as there have been incidents of hair entanglement.) Sampling must be where tests (eg dye tests - see page 69) have established that water circulates even when the pool is empty of bathers
- for pH, often on the treated water before it returns to the pool.

Expert advice may be useful in settling on the best sample point. What is important is not necessarily to get a truly representative sample point, but one that gives good conditions where it matters - in the pool.

Samples should flow from the sample point directly to the sensors, or to a flow cell fitted with sensors, as quickly as possible. Should the sample flow stop, the system should fail safe to prevent over-dosing (but with the analyser still operating).

Where the sample is taken from pipework in the plant room, it is normally satisfactory to mount the sensors close to the sample point, with little residence time between sampling and analysis.

More care is needed if the sample is taken remotely - say, some way down the poolside. The head loss in a small-bore pipe may mean that the cell does not get the minimum flow it needs; and some models are flow sensitive. On the other hand, slow moving water in a large-bore pipe may alter drastically the concentration being analysed (chlorine residual, for example, will fall). So it may be necessary to pump samples to overcome head loss and reduce time delay.

Sample pipework should be accessible, generally plastic (polyethylene or PVC is best). Steel or copper pipework is subject to chemical attack which may affect the sample quality.

Samples may need modification before analysis - eg buffering to ensure that chlorine residuals are always measured at the same pH value. This should not be necessary in pools where pH values are automatically controlled.

The time for the sample to get to the analyser, and for the sensor to register a result, should be as short as possible, but can be expected to be up to 30 seconds. This is negligibly short compared with the process time in the pool. The sensor instructs the controller almost instantaneously.

Calibration

Calibration of the chlorine monitor should be by independent analysis of the same water sample the analyser uses. It is important that calibration of free chlorine and redox monitors is always done at a constant pH value. A buffer should be used to calibrate for pH. The accuracy of the calibration technique must be greater than the accuracy required of the monitor; the monitor should be reset only if its error is greater than the acceptable limit. So the accuracy required of the monitor should be defined and maximum errors stipulated.

Although it is sensible to check the monitor daily against an appropriate chemical test, it should be enough to recalibrate the monitor monthly (more often if there are discrepancies). Typical variations between tests and automatic sensors may be as high as 15% or ±0.2 pH units. Chemical test details are described in Chapter 13, but the key issue is that the monitor is calibrated by a test that measures the same thing the monitor is set to measure.

Records of all calibration dates, results (redox, free chlorine, pH, etc) and action taken must be retained. This should include a record of pH values for calibration of free chlorine and redox.

Controllers

Electronic control units can be very sophisticated. They need to effect the appropriate change in the dosing device to maintain the set value. The simpler controllers change the dosing rate in proportion to the degree of error between the sample value and the set point - perhaps with some time delays or dead bands built in. This may be fine on fast turnover, well mixed pools - but on others can give worse conditions than manual control. There may be hunting, or cog wheel effect on a chart recorder.

More modern controllers incorporate integral and derivative as well as proportional action. This enables the controller to forecast its own action and act to prevent under or overshooting. With correct sampling, such control should be smooth and effective - although they do demand fairly sophisticated commissioning.

There are several controllers designed specifically for swimming pools. Some three-term controllers (proportional, integral, derivative) have devices that allow the unit to adapt itself to the best results possible by self-tuning. They may need to be given data such as type of pool (spa, leisure, etc) and set levels for times when there is interference (eg wave machines). Many controllers are linked to computerised building management systems, so that faults can be immediately identified and trends analysed. There are bound to be further advances - but controllers are always going to depend heavily on accurate sensors, properly calibrated, and receiving a true sample.

The PWTAG test kit research described on page 85 found instances where pool operators seemed to trust test kit readings rather than their automatic readouts. This underlines the need to establish a consistent relationship between the monitor and test kit readings. If there is a variance, it is important to find an explanation - and to check with the manufacturers if necessary.

Manufacturers' instructions on cleaning sensors should be followed exactly.

Chlorine gas system (see text for number key)

CHLORINE GAS

The system now preferred operates with the gas under pressure only at the cylinder (in the store), and uses either a cylinder-mounted chlorinator or a vacuum regulator. The rest of the dosing system is under vacuum, the loss of which produces a fail safe shutdown. The dosing system may be in the chlorine gas store; the dosing regulator is best placed near the control system.

The system is motivated by a water-operated injector fed by a booster pump, which generates sufficient vacuum to draw chlorine through flow regulating valves, gas control valves, or gas changeover devices, back to the vacuum regulator and gas cylinder. The gas mixes with the water in the throat of the injector, dissolves and is forced into the pool circulation water.

Vacuum regulator (1) This is attached directly to the cylinder, allowing gas to be drawn only when a vacuum is applied to it; otherwise, the regulator shuts off the gas; similarly if there is a valve blockage or failure. The regulators may need to be switched from one cylinder to the next, or switch over automatically.

Safety vent line (2) This is fitted with a carbon filter that destroys chlorine gas - safer than venting the automatic cylinder changeover to the outside.

Flow regulator (3) The chlorine demand in the pool determines the feed rate. This is changed manually or - better - automatically through modulation by a gas control valve and indicated by a gas flow meter. The gas is drawn from the cylinder through the flow meter and the precise quantity of chlorine is metered at a predetermined rate. A safety device within the regulator cuts the flow of gas if vacuum is lost.

Booster pump (4) Pool water from the circulation system is forced through the venturi or injector by a booster pump, also fail-safe on vacuum loss. The hydraulics must ensure that water will not flow through the injector when the booster pump is off. The pump should be electrically interlocked with the main circulation pump and controller to prevent dosing if the flow stops.

Solenoid valve   If the chlorine injector operates on mains water (rather than booster pump) it must be isolated by a solenoid valve in case the main circulation pump fails. This is best supplemented by a flow switch in the main circulation flow so that the injector can operate only with flow in the main system. Water regulations and by-laws must be followed in this.

Venturi injector (5)   Passing the boosted water through the injector creates the vacuum which is used to draw the chlorine gas from the cylinder, through the regulating valves. This mixes with the water in the injector, so that a weak chlorine solution can be returned to mix with the recirculating pool water and back to the pool. The injector is fitted with a strainer and diaphragm to stop gas flow on loss of vacuum.

Operation   The control unit must be operated only in accordance with the manufacturer's instruction manual, a copy of which must always be with the unit. The **dosing controller** (6) can be manual, or automatic by chlorine residual control

Changing cylinders and operator error are the biggest sources of accidents with chlorine gas. So a formal training policy for all operators is critical - for routine jobs and for emergencies. Written instructions must be available. The manager is responsible for this.

Protection against leaks - including **a gas warning device** (7) and **sprinkler plant** (8) - is dealt with on page 113.

Material safety data sheets (see page 102) should be incorporated, along with HSE guidance documents. Chlorine gas is highly corrosive when wet, and only approved materials and equipment can be used - and that applies also to repairs. Inspection and maintenance must also be in accordance with HSE guidance.

CIRCULATION FEEDERS

These are pieces of equipment that hold tablets of dry disinfectant. Pool water from the delivery side of the circulation pump and returning to the suction side flows over the tablets and introduces the chemicals into the pool water circulation. They are mainly used for trichloroisocyanuric acid, BCDMH and calcium hypochlorite.

Beyond that, there is some confusion about types and how they work. The challenge with such feeders is determining the rate at which the tablet dissolves or erodes, and controlling the water flow rate through the feeder (though both should be specified by the manufacturer). Water temperature affects the output, as can the amount of unused tablets in the feeders. A flow meter can be fitted.

There are often considered to be two types.
- Erosion feeders are designed so that the water flowing through them physically erodes material from the tablets without necessarily covering the entire bed of disinfectant. The material subsequently dissolves in the water circulation.
- Soaker feeders allow water to dissolve material from the tablets directly, at a rate to some extent determined by their solubility.

In practice, the distinction between the two types is not clear-cut: some feeders both erode and soak.

Safety
Although feeders are used for a variety of chemicals, it is vitally important that each feeder should be used only for what it is designed to feed - and never for a second chemical. Using the wrong chemical - calcium hypochlorite in a trichlorinator, for example - can destroy the feeder by a combination of chemical and heat attack. And if calcium hypochlorite and chlorinated isocyanurate get mixed as a result of putting both in the same feeder, nitrogen trichloride gas will be produced - with potentially explosive results, which can be fatal for the operator.

Some manufacturers and distributors do not provide the warnings necessary to prevent such accidents; they should. And the names used to describe and promote feeders do not in themselves always clearly indicate what they are to be used for.

If the pool circulation is shut down for some time, the tablets should be removed from the feeders.

Feeders should not be sited near a heat source: trichloroisocyanuric acid, for example, is very vulnerable to over-heating.

The feeders

Trichloroisocyanuric acid tablets are most commonly dosed by trichlorinators which take one to three days' supply of 300g tablets. Smaller feeders may be of an inline design on smaller pools, using up to 2in diameter pipework and 14g or 200g tablets. On larger pools the trichlorinator is normally plumbed in around the pump, relying on pressure differential. (Trichloroisocyanuric acid can also be dosed by a special feeder using flakes of trichlor in a central plastic tube surrounded with magnesium hydroxide which neutralises the pH value of the acidic trichlorinated water before it enters the pool water circulation.)

BCDMH can be dosed in special feeders called brominators. The water is shock dosed as it goes over the tablets, which are designed to last for several weeks. There are brominators designed for all sizes of pool.

Calcium hypochlorite tablets should be wetted only bit by bit, or a sludge can result. So the feeders for 300g cylindrical tablets tend to expose only the tip of each successive tablet to the water. There is also a feeder for smaller tablets, which are wetted and eroded little by little.

Feeder guidelines

To optimise safety and efficient disinfection - especially as there is some confusion about these feeders - there are important guidelines for their use.

- Chemicals and feeders must be used only as instructed; if the instructions seem unclear or incomplete, they should be checked out before using the feeder.
- Different chemicals should never be mixed - in storage or use.
- A feeder should never be used with a different chemical than the one specified. Tablets, too, should be used only in the feeders recomended. That applies to *all* combinations of chemical and feeder.
- Tablets come in various sizes. Feeders are usually designed for a particular size of tablet and size of pool. The feeder and tablets must be a match.

Chapter 11

Water circulation

Ideally swimming pool water circulation ensures that treated water reaches all areas of the pool, and polluted pool water is removed efficiently. This demands an understanding of the circulation patterns within the pool. Like the design circulation rate (see Chapter 2), circulation patterns are influenced by the depth, volume and shape of the pool tank, and by extras like moveable floors and booms.

Effective circulation requires detailed attention to overall design, surface water removal, balance tanks, inlets and outlets, flexibility, circulation pumps, and the pipework and fittings that connect it all and link it to a water treatment system sized for the turnover and circulation rate. All these are covered here, concluding with a section on dye testing

CIRCULATION DESIGN

A good circulation design will ensure:
- positive mixing of treated water with the whole pool volume. Treated water inlets can be on the pool tank walls, floors or both; wall inlets sometimes give better mixing
- the effective removal of surface water (where the bulk of the pollutants are)
- safe water outlets, normally on the base of the pool, capable of taking all of the circulation flow if for any reason surface water removal is nil
- flooded suction to circulation pumps.

There are many types of circulation design currently, but all should give better performance than those used in many older pools which may have had lower bathing loads, circulation rates, water temperatures - and lower expectations about water quality. Typical of such traditional 25m pools would be shallow end inlets, overflow (scum) channels, and a 4-hour turnover. Inlets only at one end mean dosing a higher chlorine residual to compensate for the slow turnover; scum channels do not provide good surface water

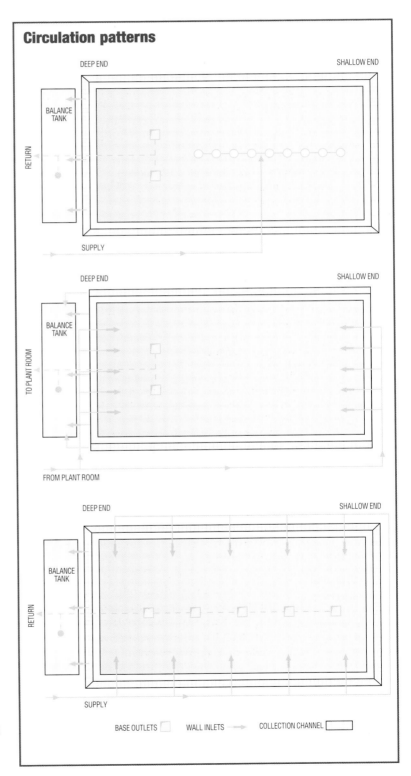

Circulation patterns

BASE OUTLETS ☐   WALL INLETS →   COLLECTION CHANNEL ☐

Leisure pool - a zonal distribution

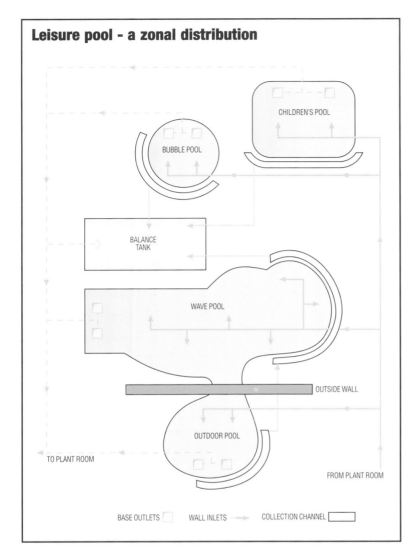

CHILDREN'S POOL

BUBBLE POOL

BALANCE TANK

WAVE POOL

OUTSIDE WALL

OUTDOOR POOL

TO PLANT ROOM

FROM PLANT ROOM

BASE OUTLETS ☐   WALL INLETS →   COLLECTION CHANNEL ☐

SURFACE WATER REMOVAL

Some unsightly, unhealthy matter remains on the surface of the water, and the majority of the organic pollution and contamination is concentrated at or near the surface irrespective of the mixing effects of the circulation system. This is also a source of potential infection. So the minimum recommendation for water removed through the surface water removal system is 20% of the circulation flow. For a healthier and more attractive pool - especially heavily-used and leisure pools - the figure should be 50-80%. Removing this proportion demands a balance tank (see below) - used as part of the hydraulic design on most new pools.

There are three basic systems for removing surface water - in decreasing order of efficiency: deck-level, overflow channels and skimmers.

Deck-level

In this system the water in the pool is at the same level as the pool surround. Water is continuously displaced over the edge and through a grid cover into a transfer channel round the perimeter of the pool. The water displaced as bathers enter the pool increases this flow. To ensure effective and uniform water removal, the leading edge of the transfer channel (ie the edge over which the water flows) should be 3mm below the pool's static water level, subject to a construction tolerance of ±2mm.

The water entering the channel is transferred to a balance tank fitted with a float valve or a sensor system operating a control valve on the suction pipework. The positive displacement of surface water means that between 50 and 100% of the circulation flow follows this route. The remainder is removed through floor outlets. Any particulate matter not removed by the latter route will settle on the pool bottom and must be removed at the end off the day (see page 127).

The water flow is gravity-driven, so the relationship between the transfer channel and the balance tank is critical. The channel (particularly its depth) and its connections with the balance tank must be sized to cope with the pool's biggest surge.

removal; a 4-hour turnover restricts the numbers that can use the pool comfortably .

A better approach would be inlets at both ends or along the length of the pool floor, surface water removal by continuous displacement into deck-level transfer channels and a 3-hour turnover. These principles can be applied to all pools.

Leisure pools, often with several pools on one treatment system, require a flexible, zonal system. Each of, say, 10 carefully chosen zones is provided with inlets on pool walls and floor, and floor outlets. All are connected to pipes with valves so that the flow to and from that particular zone can be controlled to provide the turnover appropriate to that part of the pool. If valves are not fitted, inlets need to be preset within the hydraulic design. Each zone should be flow metered at commissioning.

Overflow (scum) channels

These are common, mostly on older pools. Sills round the sides of the pool allow surface water entering them to flow through connecting pipework to the suction side of the circulation pump, usually via a suction loop. The sills must be level throughout their length so that water can be uniformly displaced into them. This system removes about 10% of the circulation flow.

Scum channels can be improved by linking them to a balance tank, but it is unlikely that they can ever be as effective as the deck-level system.

Skimmers

This method of surface water removal uses short, self-adjusting weirs installed at intervals around the sides of the pool. These deal with variations in water level arising from bather displacement. Some will remove water to a greater depth than the topmost layer of maximum pollution drawn on by a deck-level channel.

Each will remove only a small proportion of the surface water, so their efficiency as a surface water removal system will also depend on how many are used. Theoretically, enough skimmers can be fitted for the majority of the water for circulation to be removed through them. But their use in public pools should be limited by the understanding that they are unlikely to achieve the results that deck-level give.

In outdoor pools skimmers should, if possible, face the prevailing wind.

BALANCE TANKS

Balance tanks (from which water can be returned to the circulation system) are the only way of ensuring that the water remains at the optimum level for effective overflow action. They are essential to the deck-level system, and will improve a scum channel system. A balance tank also makes it possible to automate the makeup water system.

Balance tanks are normally formed as part of the concrete structure of the pool. Their accurate sizing is part of the overall hydraulic design. They need to accommodate the water displaced by bathers, plus allowances for

Minimum volume of balance tank
as % of the volume of water circulated in 1hour

Spa pools Teaching pools Splash pools Hydrotherapy pools Smaller children's pools	**20%**
School pools Lower-volume 25m competition pools (much shallow water)	**15%**
Larger-volume 25m competition pools 50m pools Diving pools	**10%**

water loss during filter backwashing and for starting up the circulation system. As a rough guide, balance tanks should have a volume of 10-20% of the hourly circulation rate. It is difficult to be exact as displacement will vary with the number of bathers, their level of activity, and the volume of water used for backwashing. But the chart above gives some guidance to minimum balance tank volumes - based on the principle that the lower the water volume to bather ratio, the larger the balance tank.

OUTLETS AND INLETS

The safety of outlets and inlets is a critical issue. Of course their covers and grills should be strong and secure enough to withstand any likely impact or vandalism. And apertures should not have gaps over 8mm, so fingers and toes cannot get caught in them. But there are more detailed design and hydraulic issues that are crucially important.

Outlets

In the light of a history of serious accidents, outlets demand very close attention. Water velocity through outlets should not exceed 0.5m/s. When calculating the size of outlets to achieve this, the free open area of the grill must be taken into account. This varies between 30 and 60% of the overall size of the grill. The relevant formulae are in the Typical pool box on the next page.

To avoid the risk of a vacuum trapping a bather on an outlet, all suction pipes that are

The typical pool

The typical pool is now shown with the connections made between water treatment plant, balance tank, transfer channel, inlets and outlets. Pipe sizes are quoted as NB - nominal bore in mm

The proportion of water removed from the surface and from the base outlets can be varied

Pipework is designed so that the total circulation rate can be removed from either the base outlets or the transfer channel

End wall inlets between swimming lanes minimise the effect of inlet system velocity

The balance tank volume is based on 15% of the circulation rate of $172m^3/h = 26m^3$

If the balance tank has the same depth as the pool's deep end, its surface area will be $13m^2$

For sizing outlets and inlets, the free open area of the grill must be calculated: it is

$$\frac{\text{Circulation rate through the grill } (m^3/h)}{0.5m/s \times 3,600}$$

The total surface area of grill (m^2) is calculated as:

$$\frac{\text{Free open area } (m^2)}{\% \text{ of outlet which is free open area}}$$

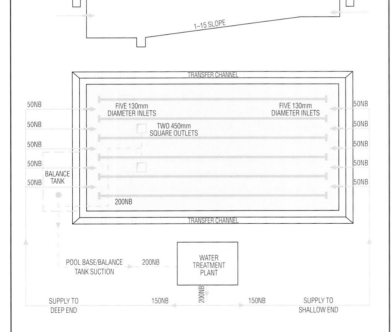

The final piece of the jigsaw - filtration - will be fitted in Chapter 12. (Pipework, outlet and inlet calculations are dealt with later in this chapter, page 70)

capable of being connected to the full suction pressure of the pump system should be connected to at least two separate outlets at least 2m apart and preferably 3m from the side walls (to avoid impact from jumping bathers). The principle is that a single bather should not be able to block all outlets from one suction pipe.

On existing pools with only one outlet, there are two options.

- A larger grill can be fitted to the outlet. It must conform to the safety principles described here.
- Additional sidewall outlets may be fitted as close as possible to the pool base and sized to meet the maximum velocity requirement above.

Wild water channels and other features can involve such large volumes of fast-flowing water that more than one outlet might lose the effect. In this case, in order for the outlet not to be covered by a single bather, it should be at least $1m^2$.

Hair entrapment   There is a useful pool outlet safety test from the US that may be included in a European standard.

- Tie a 400mm length of natural hair (about 50g) to one end of a 300mm length of 30mm diameter wooden dowel.
- Suspend the hair in pool water for 2min without tangling.
- Feed the hair into the outlet from 300mm in front and 300mm above for 2min; leave for 30sec.
- If the hair cannot be released vertically with less than 2.3kg pull, the outlet fails.

Spa pool outlets   In principle, the guidelines for conventional pools should also apply to spas. In practice, there is a problem. Most spa pools have two water circulating systems. The filtered water is normally supplied to the base area of the spa, with 100% surface water removal via a collection channel and balance tank. This avoids the need for outlets within the spa itself. A secondary system, however, normally required to operate the water jets, draws its supply from the base area of the spa. Because of the high water velocity needed for this system, even multiple outlets are likely to present a risk of hair entrapment. Spa operators should be aware of this. Spas built in to the pool building's circulation system should be able to follow PWTAG's guidelines.

Inlets

Inlets delivering water to the pool must be arranged so as to ensure that each takes its required proportion of flow. They should not stand proud of the wall or floor surfaces, or have any sharp contours. There should be enough inlets to ensure that the velocity of the water entering the pool does not generally exceed 1.5-2m/s, and perhaps as low as 0.5m/s in shallow or sensitive areas (steps, teaching points, etc) where turbulence might be a problem or where base inlets are involved. Water features like geysers, waterfalls, jets and sprays demand a far higher inlet water velocity to achieve the desired effect. It is essential, then, that safety in relation to location, etc is fully assessed. The same careful consideration should be given to inlets in pools for children and toddlers.

FLEXIBILITY

If the pool has a moveable floor, or a bulkhead (boom), the circulation system must be designed to cope with every configuration.

For moveable floors, inlets should be positioned to ensure that water is distributed above and below the floor under all operating positions. This may necessitate incorporating inlets at different levels. Water removal should be via both the surface water system and outlets in the base of the pool. The floor should incorporate apertures to allow water to pass through the floor, maintain the distribution within the structure and avoid pollution buildup in any dead spots.

Bulkheads, either laterally moveable or submergible, must incorporate apertures sufficient to maintain the circulation system in all operating positions. Where a submerged boom is housed in a deep channel in the base of the pool, water should be extracted from the base of the channel to maintain circulation.

CIRCULATION PUMPS

Pools should have sufficient pump volume/head capacity to achieve the required pool turnover period. Standby pumping capacity should be provided to allow the plant to continue to function at full flow if one of the pumps has failed. The pumping system should be capable of reduced flow rates at

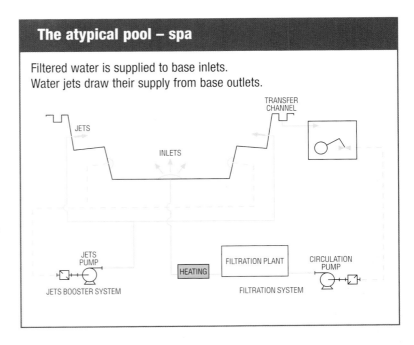

The atypical pool – spa

Filtered water is supplied to base inlets.
Water jets draw their supply from base outlets.

night when appropriate. Three, half-capacity pumps provide flexibility: motors and pumps can be rested in rotation, and turnover and energy use can be reduced during closed periods, without compromising water quality. Variable speed drives can be used to control pump flow efficiently.

With all pools, it is vital that the circulation rates for specified turnover periods should be maintained by the pump (or pumps) when the filters are dirty (offering the maximum resistance in the system) and taking into account any extra processes such as ozone and UV. For example, incorporating ozone may increase the overall headloss by 4-6m; UV by 3-4m

The pumps and their layout should be designed in accordance with the manufacturer's recommendations, and their performance guaranteed. There are self-priming pumps normally running at 2,900rpm - but most systems use standard centrifugal pumps running at 1,450rpm. It is best for these to be located below pool water level and thus permanently primed. The distance between pumps and pool outlets/balance tanks should be minimised to reduce the overall friction loss on the suction side of the pumps. This ensures that the pump operates as efficiently as possible and maximises its lifespan. If they cannot be close, the suction pipework size may need to be increased to reduce friction and thus ensure acceptably low pressure drop.

They must also be arranged to give the requisite flow for backwashing. Backwashing should use pool water, so that it is replaced with fresh mains water. This has the important advantage of diluting the pool water (see page 11) and so limiting the build-up of pollutants.

Circulation pipework

Pipework systems should be sized to limit water velocities below levels which cause excessive headloss due to friction, reducing the life of valves, strainer boxes, etc. Velocities can be slightly higher in the delivery than in the suction pipework - though the resulting increase in headloss within the system must be taken into account when sizing the circulation pumps. As the graph below shows, headloss varies in proportion to the square of the velocity - which underlines the need to limit velocities, particularly on the suction side.

For example, the friction loss at a velocity of 3m/sec is 9 times that at 1m/sec.

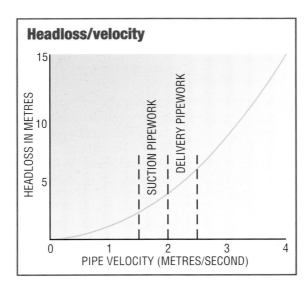

As a guide that conforms with good engineering practice, pipe velocities should be:
- suction   1.5m/sec
- delivery   2-2.5m/sec.

There has to be a slight allowance on these figures for different pipe sizes but suction velocities should never exceed 2.0m/sec.

Distribution pipework around the pool must be pressure tested - particularly if it is going to be buried in or under the pool structure. The methods should form part of the specification. Buried pipework must be supported against stresses following manufacturers' instructions.

Strainer boxes

Each circulation pump impeller needs protection from hair, plasters, straps, jewellery, etc by a strainer box fitted to the suction side of every pump, or a single box on the main suction line. The strainer basket is usually uPVC or stainless steel, with a mesh size of about 3mm, inside a strainer box of stainless steel, or uPVC/GRP. A spare basket for use while the other is cleaned minimises pump shutdown time.

Valves

The main valves are usually the butterfly type installed between the pipework flanges - compact and cost-effective. The valve materials must be suitable for the application: for example, those in contact with ozonated water must be of a higher specification than for chlorinated water.

Valves up to 150mm bore are normally lever-lock operated. To prevent possible shock pressure from surges, butterfly valves above 150mm bore should be gear operated, to limit the speed of opening and closing the valves.

Heat exchangers

Heat exchangers normally operate on a bypass from the main delivery line to the pool. A separate pumping unit to the heat exchanger is the best way of ensuring the correct water volume through it; no extra load on the main circulating pumps. Depending on the temperature in the heat exchanger, stainless steel rather than uPVC may be needed for its pipework.

Instrumentation

All installations should have sufficient instrumentation to measure the performance of the system and should include:
- a flow meter or meters to measure the circulation rate and the backwash rate of each filter
- inlet and outlet (or differential pressure) gauges on each filter to measure the headloss across the sand bed
- a water meter on the makeup water system
- flow metering for dilution
- an electricity meter for the whole pool plant, within the filtration panel - although it is not essential and is expensive.

Suction and delivery or differential pressure gauges on each circulation pump (including those for features) are also desirable.

The designer/installer of the system should at commissioning prove by measurement the performance of the system, and the readings taken should be documented in the operating and maintenance manuals for future reference.

More than one pool

Where an establishment contains two or more pools, then - depending on size and use - each should ideally have a separate set of circulation pumps and filters. Valved cross-connections on the circulation pipework can be provided to facilitate interchange of pumps and filters in an emergency. With pools of similar size and/or circulation rate, the pools have to be at the same temperature. If there is a separate, small pool at a far lower circulation rate (spa or bubble pool, for example), taking the heated water directly from the heat exchanger outlet to that pool first can maintain a reasonable temperature difference. (Full heat loss calculations will need to be be done at the design stage.)

A single system for two or more pools is less frequently used, and greater care must then be taken to ensure that the hydraulics, chemical monitoring, dosing, etc are properly designed. The water temperature requirements must be assessed. A smaller pool, for example, can be maintained at a slightly higher temperature, but the temperature difference relates directly to the heat losses within the systems.

DYE TESTING

The purpose of dye testing is to confirm the effectiveness of water distibution - both its design and its installation. There are three main stages.

Material compatibility

Before the test, the proposed dye must be checked to establish that it does not stain or otherwise attack the pool tank, fittings, tiles, grout, sealant, moveable floors, booms, etc. It is wise to check all pool surfaces at this stage, for cleanliness and discolouration, in case of subsequent dispute.

Setting up the hydraulics

It must be established that the pool edge is within the agreed tolerance (normally ±2mm) to ensure uniform surface water removal. Also, that the correct proportion of water is drawn from the pool base and surface. Inlet and

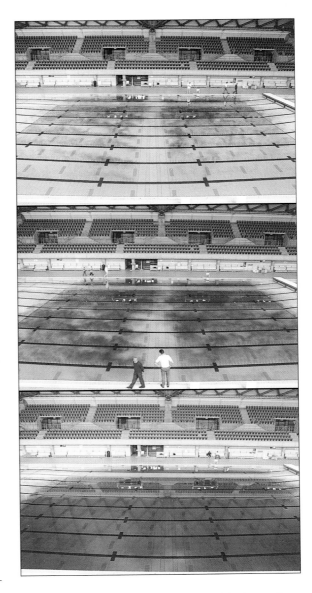

A dye test at Pond's Forge pool in Sheffield. Photographs taken after 5 minutes, 11 minutes and 17 minutes

outlet flow should be checked and balanced; the design circulation rate established

The test

The main dye used is Eriochrome black T $(0.2g/m^3$ of circulation). The pool water is first de-chlorinated using sodium thiosulphate or equivalent (see page 83). Any ozone treatment plant or carbon filters are bypassed (and the flow rate restored to what it was before the bypass); other filters not bypassed must be clean. The circulation is switched off. The dye is then added to the pool close to the chlorine dosing point, usually through a chemical dosing pump or strainer box. The normal circulation rate is resumed.

The time taken for the pool water to become evenly coloured gives a measure of the adequacy of the distribution system. As a

Base extraction and balance tank suction lines, together with main return to the plant room, should be sized to take the total circulation rate.

Main pool suction
Circulation rate 172m³/h
Recommended velocity 1.5m/s (2m/s max)
200mm bore line pipe would give 1.55m/s
This would be acceptable.

Main pool delivery
Circulation rate 172m³/h
Recommended velocity 2-2.5m/s
As 150mm bore line pipework would have a velocity in excess of this, 200mm line should be used.

Delivery to each end of the pool
The flow to each end should be based on 50% of total, so 86m³/h
Recommended velocity 2-2.5m/s
As 100mm bore line pipework would have a velocity in excess of this, a 150mm pipe should be used, which will result in a velocity of 1.35m/s.

Flow rate
Based on above, the flow through each inlet (five inlets at each end of the pool)

Flow rate $\frac{86}{5}$ = 17.2m³/h

Recommended velocity 2-2.5m/s
50mm bore pipe would give 2.1m/s. This is acceptable

Sizing outlet grills
Recommended velocity 0.5m/s; Minimum of two outlets
Assume the outlets are to be square with free open area of 30%:

Flow through each outlet $\frac{172}{2}$ = 86m³/h

Free open area $\frac{86}{0.5 \times 3600}$ = 0.0478m²

Surface area of grill $\frac{0.0478}{0.3}$ = 0.159m²

Grill size 0.41 metres square
A standard grill size of 450mm square is used

Sizing inlet fittings
Recommended velocity 1.5m/s
Assuming the fitting is circular with a free open area of 25%:

Free open area $\frac{17.2}{1.5 \times 3600}$ = 0.00319m²

Surface area of grill $\frac{0.00319}{0.25}$ = 0.0127m²

This gives a grill diameter of 130mm.

percentage of the turnover period:
50% is satisfactory
25% is excellent.

Once the colouration of the pool is completed, the dye should be removed without delay using chlorine, ozone or equivalent. This addition can serve as a second, comfirmatory test of circulation. So 5ppm chlorine, for example, should clear the dye colour as quickly as it spread.

Entrained air

Pool water will sometimes appear aerated and thus slightly turbid (white, milky). Entrained air is difficult to get rid of - and often difficult to explain. In theory air can get into the pool's circulation system only where its pressure is below atmospheric. That means the suction side of circulating pumps, on venturi-type devices and on high-level loops. The commonest source of problems seems to be the first of these, via the surface water removal system, strainer box seals, valve joints or within the mechanical seals in the pumping unit.

A correctly designed balance tank system avoids air entrainment from surface water removal, but other surface water removal methods - anti-syphon loop devices, for example - can be the culprits.

Chapter 12

Filtration

Clarity of pool water is critical. It should be possible to see the bottom of the pool at its deepest point. If not, there is an immediate physical danger to anyone in distress, as well as the likelihood of discomfort to bathers. Also, disinfection will be compromised by reduced clarity. In practice, it must be possible to see a small child on the bottom of the deep end; some operators aim to be able to call heads or tails on a coin lying on the bottom. In terms of nephelometric turbidity units, 0.5NTU is a useful upper limit guideline.

Clarity is reduced by turbidity - colloidal or particulate matter in suspension in the water. It is important to know the source - whether pollution from bathers, external contamination, inadequate circulation/turnover or disinfection, or incorrect use of water treatment chemicals - in case this can be dealt with directly. The likeliest remedy, however, is adequate filtration and backwashing, coupled with coagulation (flocculation) to convert the colloids into a filterable flocculus, or floc.

There are a number of factors to be taken into account when specifying filters - including the overall purification system. But the baseline is that there must be enough filter capacity to cope with the design circulation rate (established as in Chapter 3).

SAND FILTRATION

Sand filters are recommended for all non-domestic swimming pools. Cheaper alternatives (cartridge filters and pre-coat or diatomaceous earth filters) cannot always be relied on to cope with the bathing conditions that municipal and commercial pools must expect at peak times. They also demand more care and attention than sand filters. Other, sometimes more expensive filter media are either for specialist use (eg carbon filters for deozonation, etc - see page 73) or of doubtful extra value (eg zeolite - page 44).

Filtration rates
In general, the greater the filtration velocity, the lower the filtration efficiency. In practice, efficiency falls off even more rapidly at velocities of over 30m/h ($m^3/m^2/h$). This can be demonstrated experimentally, using standard water tests for pollution. Sand filtration can be achieved by rapid gravity: the water passes through the sand bed in open-top filters, so velocity is related directly to the static head of water above the bed. Alternatively, pressure is generated inside a sealed filter vessel - which is the normal method in swimming pools.

Filter ratings are based on sand filtration rates. The three categories are ranges only:
- low-rate   up to 10m/h
- medium-rate   11 to 30m/h
- high-rate   31 to 50m/h

The loss of pressure through the filter is directly proportional to filtration velocity within the range of 10-25m/h. So, for conventional public pools where bathing loads are consistently high, a medium filtration rate of 10-25m/h is recommended. The filtration system should be based on the design maximum bathing load, operating 24h a day, ideally designed so that the circulation rate can be reduced overnight or during quieter periods. If the filtration rate is reduced overnight, the rate should be increased again slowly. Sudden increases can detach deposits within the filter bed and result in material getting into the pool. If rate reduction has been achieved by shutting down one or more circulation pumps, it is essential to restart each pump against a closed valve, then slowly open the valve to achieve the desired flow rate.

Medium-rate filters are recommended for all non-domestic pools including those hotel and school pools subject to loading demands similar to those experienced by conventional pools.

High-rate filters do not handle particles and colloids as effectively as medium-rate filters.

Such materials tend to pass through the sand bed. Coagulants are irrelevant, as the floc would tend not to be trapped in the filter. So the water treatment guidelines in this book cannot be applied to pools with high-rate filters.

Where high-rate filters are considered - for reasons of economy in small pools - it is clearly important that attention is paid to the anticipated bathing load. Where this might be increased, perhaps with wider use of the pool, high-rate filters would certainly be inadvisable.

Low-rate filters, though very efficient, are not much used in pools because of the large surface area needed.

The sand bed

The right bed depth, like flow rate, is important for efficient filtration. A depth of 1m is acceptable for medium-rate filters - whether single or multi-grade. Both types have advantages.

Single-grade beds have about 800mm of sand. The precise depth depends on the size of grain. Most filter sand is graded in a 1:2 size ratio, eg 0.5-1mm (16/30: the usual size in the UK) and 1-2mm. The finer it is, the shallower the bed can be. Underneath there will be a layer of coarse-grade media (a few mm in size). This can help the dispersion of backwashed water from the slotted nozzles below, needed as part of the underdrain system.

Multi-grade beds contain a number of layers of coarse media under about 550mm of sand. The coarse media offer less resistance to backwash water, so are less likely to need air scour (see next page). The underdrain system is a series of perforated pipes rather than nozzles - less complex. But the need for each coarse grade to be level makes installation and refilling after maintenance more difficult than with single-grade filters.

Underdrains

Underdrains must collect filtered water, and distribute backwash water, evenly. They must be supported properly - concrete is good - to avoid damage as operating conditions change. Diaphragm plates are not recommended because when they deteriorate, the side of the filter shell and the lining may corrode. The lining is very difficult to refurbish. Any dead space beneath underdrains of the header and lateral types must be filled with concrete (not gravel) to avoid stagnant water areas where microorganisms may proliferate.

Number of filters

Pools will benefit greatly from the increased flexibility and the safeguards of having more than one filter. In particular, the pool can carry on with a reduced turnover on one filter while the other is being inspected or worked on. Ideally, filtered water from one filter should be used to backwash another.

Single-grade filter

MANHOLE
BULK AND AUTO AIR RELEASE
INLET
VIEWING WINDOW
FILTER SAND
250mm MINIMUM DIA. SAND HOLE
COARSE MEDIA (VARIOUS GRADES)
SLOTTED OR PERFORATED LATERAL SYSTEM
COLLECTION SYSTEM SUPPORT (CONCRETED)
OUTLET

Multi-grade filter

MANHOLE
BULK AND AUTO AIR RELEASE
INLET
VIEWING WINDOW
FILTER SAND
250mm MINIMUM DIA. SAND HOLE
COARSE SAND
LATERAL SYSTEM WITH SLOTTED NOZZLES
COLLECTION SYSTEM SUPPORT (CONCRETED)
OUTLET

Backwashing

Backwashing is critically important for good filtration. Passing pool water back through the filters to waste is an essential routine in caring for the filters and diluting the pool with fresh water. It should be done whenever the the loss of pressure across the filter reaches the level recommended by the filter manufacturer; but certainly at least once a week. Even if care is taken not to reduce significantly the depth of the water in the pool, backwashing should, ideally, not be done during bathing: active disinfection will stop during backwash, and some leisure areas may drain altogether.

A 5-minute wash may clean the bed adequately, but a viewing window on the filter outlet is the only way to check progress; backwashing should continue until the backwash water is clear; the manufacturer's recommendations should also be taken into account. After backwashing, the normal flow should be restarted, but the filter should run to waste for a few minutes, which allows the newly-expanded filter bed to settle, and dirt in the pipework to drain off.

The backwash flow must be fast enough to fluidise the sand bed - about 30m/h (for 0.5-1mm sand; coarser grains may require a faster flow). Air scouring first - at about 32m/h at 0.35bar - can help clean the media, as can filter design. A viewing port (window) to show the top of the sand bed will allow operators to check that fluidisation is achieved. (The manufacturer's recommendations are critical.) Backwash flow rates should not be so high that the bed expands beyond the overflow level. The backwash water pipework must be large enough to discharge the washwater without a build up of pressure inside the filter tank. And of course the pumps must be able to cope with the work.

Backwash water is classified as a trade effluent. So consent has to be sought from the relevant water authorities about the nature, volume and frequency of the discharge from backwashing and dilution (see page 12).

If the drainage system cannot deal with the backwash flow rate, a backwash water holding tank (*not* a balance tank) may have to be installed. It is sized to take at least one backwash plus 20%, and should have an alarm or shut-off to avoid flooding.

The limits of filtration

The average pore size of a pool sand filter depends on the size of sand used, but can be as low as 100μm. The nature of progressive filtration, however, means that more and more can be filtered out in successive passes through the filter. So there is no specific bottom limit to the size of particle that can be removed. With the aid of a coagulant, a single pass at an appropriate flow rate can remove almost completely all suspended matter - including colloidal matter smaller than 1μm. High-rate filters cannot achieve the same standard, because true filtration is compromised and supplanted by sieving.

Carbon filtration

Carbon is widely used in industry and elsewhere for filtration - but in swimming pools mainly for deozonation (see page 48) and removal of organics. Carbon works by both filtration and adsorption of materials onto its surface. There are two types of carbon used.

- Hydroanthracite is a version of anthracite coal with no internal structure and a surface area of 150-300m²/g. It mainly filters, with very little adsorption.
- Activated carbon is produced by steam treatment from coconut shell, coal or wood. It has a highly developed internal pore structure which gives it an effective surface area of 1,000m²/g. This makes it a more efficient adsorption medium - though pore distribution, hardness, purity and particle size are also important.

In a deozonising filter, carbon will remove ozone, chlorine and - with activated carbon particularly - organic contaminants. The chlorine removal makes the lower reaches of the filter vulnerable to microbiological colonisation - particularly, it seems, by *Pseudomonas aeruginosa*, sometimes protected in clumps in association with biofilm or even other microorganisms. This is one reason why carbon filters promoted for chloramine removal have proved a very mixed blessing. In any case, filter design and flow and backwash rates are particularly critical with carbon filters.

Carbon filters do not reduce the level of total dissolved solids (TDS); so such filters must not be used as a substitute for adequate dilution unless they demonstrate that they are reducing organics and chloramines over a period of time.

FILTER DESIGN AND CONSTRUCTION

Pressure sand filters are usually of the vertical, downward-flow type; horizontal filters are less flexible in operation and maintenance. Vertical filters also tend to give more even distribution of water.

Prefabricated mild steel has been the usual material of construction. Correctly manufactured, maintained and refurbished (including relining), steel filters should last at least 25 years. Mild steel filter vessels need to be lined internally to protect against corrosion. If there is a flaw in the selection of lining material, preparation of the steel, or application of the lining, premature failure may result. If the client (or consultant) specifies the lining, the responsibility for any failure might be difficult to place with the contractor. If the contractor takes responsibility for the specification, with a five-year guarantee, then failures should be less problematical contractually - provided the company lasts five years.

Stainless steel has proved successful, but cost limits its application to other than small units.

Glass-fibre filters are now commonly available in sizes up to 3m diameter and with filtration rates up to 50m/h. But it is not recommended that the rate should exceed 25m/h for public

Filters

pools (see page 71). The glass-fibre construction is resistant to corrosion from water and pool chemicals, although they have a limited track record, particularly with the use of ozone. Replacement of glass-fibre filters (particularly the larger diameter units) may be difficult because of access restrictions into and round the plant room. On the other hand, some manufacturers claim a life of 20 years for a well-maintained glass-fibre filter.

Concrete filters, which operate by gravity rather than pressure, and are more commonly used in potable water treatment systems, have also been used in some pools, particularly outdoors.

Specifications

Filters should be designed to the appropriate British Standard for the type of filter and material used in its construction, and it is recommended that certain quality and performance standards should be specified.

- Shells of mild steel plate should be of a thickness capable of being tested to 3.5 bar and operating at approximately 2.5 bar. They should be prepared in accordance with the manufacturer's recommendations, being manufactured to good commercial practice procedures and generally in accordance with BS 5500 where appropriate.
- Stainless steel shells should be high quality (316L or better), and resistant to the chemicals used in pool water treatment.
- Filter shell linings are vulnerable to the aggressive conditions (flow rates, chemicals, temperatures, etc) of pool water. See this page for safeguards.
- The water distribution and collection system should be constructed of corrosion-resistant materials. It should give an even collection of filtered water, an even distribution of unfiltered water and air and water during backwash.
- An automatic air eliminator and a safe, manually operated quick air release mechanism should be fitted to each filter.
- To measure the differential pressure across filter beds during operation, gauges should be fitted which indicate the pressure at the top and bottom of the filters.
- A flow meter should be fitted (and regularly serviced) to indicate normal water flow and backwash rates.
- The system should be capable of providing a backwash flow of a rate and duration to

suit the manufacturer's recommendation, which can also include the requirement of an air scour process. The backwash water flow rate must not be less than the rate necessary for the fluidisation of the filter bed as specified by the manufacturer.

- Provision should be made for a backwash drain of an appropriate capacity.
- It should be possible to observe the clarity of the effluent water throughout the period of the filter backwashing. Normally a visual method, such as full-bore illumination of the wash-water outlet pipe or a branched sight glass, will be installed.
- The provision of one or two viewing ports (usually perspex windows) on the filter will allow backwashing to be observed.

Maintenance

Filters should be opened up and inspected internally at least once a year by someone familiar with the sort of problems that can appear. That means attention to sand quality, under-drains and corrosion. Unusual signs - fissures, an uneven bed, mud balling, etc - need investigation. Any remedial work will need to be done by specialist contractors - perhaps under a maintenance contract. Filter media may need to be topped up each year and replaced every 5-7 years. (There is more advice on maintaining filters and associated equipment in Chapter 21.)

COAGULATION

Coagulants (sometimes called flocculants) enhance the removal of dissolved, colloidal or suspended material by bringing it out of solution or suspension as solids (coagulation), then clumping the solids together (flocculation), producing a floc which is more easily trapped in a filter. Coagulants help gather up bacteria generally, but are particularly crucial in helping filter two classes of material which otherwise would pass through the filter:

- the infective cysts of *Cryptosporidium* and *Giardia* - small and resistant to disinfectant (see page 88)
- humic acid - a significant precursor of unwelcome trihalomethanes (see page 94)
- phosphates.

Coagulants will be less effective where pH values are above the recommended operating range. A minimum alkalinity of about 75mg/l as $CaCO_3$ is required for effective flocculation.

Ozone treatment breaks down colloids and encourages microflocculation; so a coagulant may not be needed. However, ozone is at its most efficient when applied to water that has been treated with a coagulant and filtered. Certainly, if the water is dull, not sparkling, the use of alum or PAC may be appropriate.

The coagulants

Alum (aluminium sulphate, kibbled alum), PAC (polyaluminium chloride or aluminium hydroxychloride), PASS (polyaluminium sulpho-silicate), sodium aluminate, iron chlorides and iron sulphates have all been used in pool water clarification. Chemically they behave in similar ways: they form a gelatinous precipitate by hydrolysis. Aluminium-based coagulants operate best at pH values between 6.5 and 7.2; iron salts between 6.5 and 7.5. Iron salts may, however, leave an iron residual and this must be kept very low to prevent staining; they are not used widely in the UK.

Dosing coagulants

Dosing should be by means of chemical dosing pumps. Where coagulants are dosed continuously, the pumps must be capable of dosing accurately the small quantities required, and also be capable of adjustment to the requirements of the bathing load. This is particularly important for PAC. Hand dosing coagulant, or placing it in the strainer box, is not acceptable.

In a recycling system like a swimming pool it is important that coagulants do not build up or reach the pool in any appreciable concentrations. It is also important that the gelatinous floc does not impair filtration by causing blockage or breakthrough. The key to this is low dosage rates and good backwash frequency.

Alum and sodium aluminate are powders or granules which are normally prepared as 5% solutions. The traditional dose in the UK - approximately 20mg/l for the period of one pool turnover after backwashing the filters - is not recommended. It is bad for swimmers and bad for pool water. Instead, filtration studies and European practice have shown that improved filtration can be achieved by continuous dosing; this is recommended. The minimum continuous dose is 0.05mg/l as aluminium (for aluminium-based coagulants); 0.1mg/l for iron.

The typical pool is now complete - with two filters and three circulating pumps. The filter specifications are:
vertical diameter 2.2m
filter area 7.6m² total
filtration rate 22.63m/h
backwash rate 30m/h

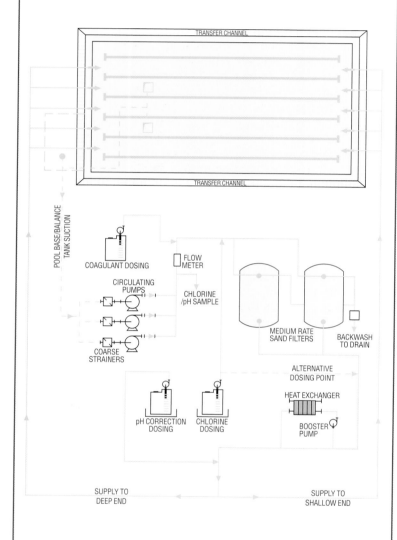

For alum solutions, the dosing pump will need to draw 5% alum from a tank fitted with a stirrer in which the alum solution has previously been prepared. Caution should be taken to avoid overdosing, as heavy doses of aluminium sulphate may cause a depression in the pH value, and consequent problems with chlorination and corrosion. Alum will also contribute to sulphate levels, that can attack concrete and grout (see page 80). There is a simple colour test to establish if alum is breaking through the filter.

PAC is directly and continuously dosed from the containers in which it is delivered at a rate of about $0.1ml/m^3$.

Coagulant dosing is not recommended on high-rate (as opposed to medium-rate) filters, as material is more likely to pass through the sand bed. The depth of the sand bed is also significant: the deeper, within the usual limits (see page 72) the better. Velocity and depth will need to be considered together.

Injection Following the injection of coagulant, coagulation of pollutants happens quite quickly. Flocculation is a slower process, so it is important that the injection point ensures that coagulant mixes well with the circulation water and the residence time is long enough for the desired flocculation (at least 10sec at a flow velocity not exceeding 1.5m/sec), before the water reaches the filter media. Even this may not be long enough, but the sand bed acts as a flocculator and floc is formed as the water passes through.

Injection points should be located well away from sampling points for chlorine residual or pH value determinations, because localised high concentrations may give a false picture of water quality. For safety reasons, they should also be sited away from other dosing points.

Bring on the bathers

Chapter 13

Chemical control

Pool water requires more attention than just the appropriate level of residual disinfection. The pool might be discoloured and cloudy (turbid); dissolved substances can be deposited; the water may be corrosive; pH values may need to be adjusted for efficient disinfection. So, for the disinfectant to work properly, and for all-round good water quality, dosing with other chemicals may be necessary.

A principle underlying successful control of water quality is choosing a disinfectant suitable for the mains water - see page 31. Coagulants, which improve the removal of suspended matter by filtration, are dealt with on page 75. Dilution with fresh water is also important here (see page 11).

This chapter deals with the control - with the minimum of chemical dosing - of the most important water quality factors. It details their relative importance and the principles that underpin monitoring water quality. It also deals in detail with testing regimes for the chlorine disinfectants, their byproducts and other chemical parameters. (Data for other disinfectants are covered in Chapters 7-9.)

pH VALUE

The degree of acidity or alkalinity (sometimes called basicity) of a water is measured in terms of its pH value. A pH value of 7 is neutral; a value falling below 7 indicates an increasing degree of acidity; rising above 7 indicates an increasing degree of alkalinity. As pH value is measured on a logarithmic scale, each unit up or down represents a tenfold difference in alkalinity/acidity.

Adjustment of the pH value of pool water is essential.

- The bactericidal action of most disinfectants depends on pH, and it is therefore necessary to maintain the pH value within the optimum effective range for each disinfectant. For example, the

bactericidal efficacy of chlorination decreases rapidly as the pH value rises towards 8. (See graph page 38.)
- As the pH value rises towards 8, the water also has an increasing tendency to encourage precipitation of hardness salts.
- As the pH value falls below 7, the water becomes increasingly corrosive to pool materials.
- If the pH value is too low or too high, the water can irritate the skin and eyes.
- Coagulants are significantly less effective if the pH value goes above the recommended range.
- Residual analysis needs a steady pH.

These factors suggest different pH values, so there is no ideal value, but an optimum for each disinfection system. In practice, it is sufficient to keep the pH value within a range for each disinfectant (see under *Disinfectants in use* in Chapter 5). Operators using chlorine-based disinfectants should aim for the bottom of the recommended range (7.2-7.4 better than 7.2-7.8) where disinfection is most effective. This, and lower-than-traditional chlorine residuals, should be perfectly possible if this book's guidelines on control etc are followed. If lowering the pH is followed by worsening water quality, clearly some other action must be taken.

Controlling pH value

In order to maintain the pH value within the recommended range, regular measurements are essential, and adjustment either continuously or intermittently is usually necessary. For heavily used pools, the pH value should be measured continuously and adjusted automatically; for other pools it is sufficient to measure the pH value regularly and adjust it intermittently. Occasionally a pool will not require the addition of acid or alkali for pH value control - due to a particular combination of water quality characteristics and disinfectant use. However, this cannot be reliably predicted, so it is essential to provide for the dosing of pH value adjustment chemicals.

The chemical required for pH value adjustment will generally depend on whether the disinfectant used is itself alkaline or acidic.

Alkaline disinfectants   Sodium and calcium hypochlorite normally require only the addition of an acid for pH value correction - perhaps a solution of sodium bisulphate (dry acid). Too much sulphate can bring corrosion problems - see page 80. Carbon dioxide can be used as an acid to control pH value - but with limitations. In general, CO_2 works best at reducing pH value where the total alkalinity of mains water is less than 150mg/l as $CaCO_3$ and hardness less than 300mg/l as $CaCO_3$. Otherwise, hydrochloric acid or sodium bisulphate are more effective and cheaper. Hydrochloric acid is best diluted with the venturi distribution system on page 53.

Acidic disinfectants   Chlorine gas and trichloroisocyanuric acid will normally require the addition of an alkali - usually a solution of sodium carbonate (soda ash) - to raise pH value. Chlorine may also need sodium bicarbonate, to increase alkalinity rather than pH value - see Alkalinity section below. Other alkalis, such as sodium hydroxide (caustic soda) could be used, but they are not recommended for swimming pools, because they are difficult to handle and control. The use of a solid dolomitic material in the filters to control the pH value automatically may be considered for the more acidic disinfectants. But it is an inflexible treatment: it establishes a pH value that cannot then be changed. If used, it should be from a separate dosing feeder.

Testing for pH value

The influence of pH value on disinfection is critical, but it is important to avoid the swings in pH value caused by the intermittent addition of treatment chemicals. In fact pH value is relatively easy to control: where tests indicate stability, manual tests need be done only as often as disinfectant tests. Test kits based on chemical reagents (indicators) or on electrical instruments using glass pH electrodes are widely available. Manufacturers' instructions should be followed. Dedicated cells should be used for pH determination.

Guidelines for action to be taken on test results depend on the disinfectant being used and the calculation of water balance. It is important that the pH value is kept relatively low to speed disinfection, and possibly help

coagulation, but sufficiently high to contain the production of irritants with chlorine or bromine-based systems.

ALKALINITY

The total alkalinity of a water is a measure of the alkaline salts dissolved in it - bicarbonates and carbonates mainly. The higher the alkalinity the more resistant the water is to pH value change: the alkalinity buffers the water. So 'pH bounce' - large changes in pH value in response to changes in the dosage levels of disinfectant and pH correction chemical - is prevented, as long as total alkalinity is above 75mg/l as $CaCO_3$. (That is also the minimum for effective coagulation.) Conversely, alkalinity above 200mg/l can make any necessary pH adjustment difficult ('pH lock').

Within that range, all that matters is that the alkalinity does not interfere with maintaining a stable pH value appropriate to the disinfectant used. So even if the alkalinity settles persistently at, say, 50mg/l, this is satisfactory as long as the pH value is stable.

The graph below shows in a little more detail how pH value reacts to the addition of acidic or alkaline chemicals (some disinfectants, for example).

The plateau with relatively little change in pH value as the acid or alkali is added is a measure of the alkalinity. The longer the plateau - ie the more alkaline materials there are dissolved in the water - the more acid it

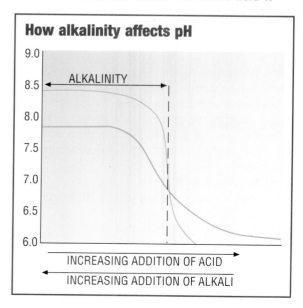

takes to lower the pH value - with the pH value falling slowly to start with. Then, when more acid or alkali is added, the pH value suddenly changes with the addition of a relatively small amount of acid or alkali.

Strong acids (eg sodium bisulphate or hydrochloric acid) and strong alkali (eg caustic soda) give a sharp change in pH value once the alkalinity or acidity has been used up. Weak acids (eg carbon dioxide) and weak alkalis (eg sodium bicarbonate) give shallower curves, but it is easier to build up a large alkalinity without a high pH value.

Controlling alkalinity

Alkalinity should be measured weekly, using alkalinity test tablets. If alkalinity has to be increased (because it is below 75mg/l as $CaCO_3$), sodium bicarbonate is the standard chemical: 1.7kg added for each $50m^3$ of pool water should increase total alkalinity by 20mg/l without affecting the pH value unduly.

If the alkalinity seems high (over 200mg/l), and an acid disinfectant is used, simply waiting may see it come down. If not, dilution should do it. If the water is naturally very alkaline, nothing should be done unless there is pH lock. If there is pH lock, sodium bisulphate solution should be used: 2.4kg added for each $50m^3$ of pool water should reduce total alkalinity by 20mg/l (though this may affect pH value). Ten litres of 15% hydrochloric acid should give the same result.

A tank and pump may be installed for dosing alkalinity chemicals. If not, the pool should be empty of bathers before hand dosing.

HARDNESS

The total hardness of a water is a measure of all its calcium and magnesium salts, such as carbonates, bicarbonates, sulphates and chlorides. Temporary hardness is that part of the total hardness which precipitates from the water on boiling; it consists of calcium and magnesium carbonates and bicarbonates. Permanent hardness is the part which does not precipitate from the water on boiling; it consists of other calcium and magnesium salts such as sulphates and chlorides.

Calcium hardness is that part of the total hardness consisting of calcium salts, and is the

measure particularly relevant to swimming pools. It should be checked weekly, with tablets. To raise hardness, calcium chloride at 1.5kg for each $50m^3$ of pool water will increase calcium hardness by about 20mg/l. To lower hardness, dilution is the only solution - and then only if the mains water is relatively soft. But what level of hardness is satisfactory?

If calcium hardness is below about 40mg/l as $CaCO_3$, the water is likely to be corrosive to the fabric of the pool plant. By about 75mg/l a protective scale can start to form; so as far as corrosion is concerned, there should be no need to boost hardness beyond that. Ideally, all elements of the pool should be able to withstand water at that sort of level. Unfortunately, the problem of cementitious grout loss has been blamed by some on low hardness; their solution is to boost hardness (perhaps by using calcium hypochlorite instead of sodium hypochlorite) as high as 400 mg/l.

Yet others claim to know of no theoretical or practical basis for maintaining high hardness figures. Given the variability in water supplies and experience with pools around the country, it seems difficult to summon up good evidence that hardness is the issue. Acids are known to attack grout, as do sulphates - see below. Water movement (wave machines, for example) will erode grout - as might automatic cleaners. Application standards may well be an issue: for example, it can be difficult to achieve the recommended 90% fill of the void behind tiles; there is also the question of whether grout is given enough time to cure before the pool is filled. The different gaps between different sizes of tiles may even be part of the problem.

Grout loss seems to be less of a problem abroad, without boosting hardness into the hundreds. On the other hand, epoxy grouts - which do resist attack - seem to be used more commonly abroad. The roughly £40,000 cost of tiling and grouting a 25m pool rises to just £44,000 if epoxy is used instead of cementitious grout. This extra could be less than the chemical cost of increasing hardness.

More work is needed on the problem. Meanwhile, PWTAG's view is that pool water should be maintained for bathers' comfort, and that grout should withstand that water. So the recommendation is to maintain calcium hardness at between 75 and 150mg/l as

CaCO₃. Higher than that, unwelcome scale and deposits may even mask the problem at the expense of water quality. If pool designers and managers are still nervous about the effects of low levels of hardness, they should seriously consider epoxy grout.

DISSOLVED SOLIDS

Total dissolved solids (TDS) is the sum of the weight of soluble material in water. Mains water often has a TDS of several hundred mg/l, except in soft water areas where it is considerably lower. Disinfectants and other pool chemicals will inevitably increase TDS levels significantly - of chloride and sulphate in particular. Bather and other pollution will also increase levels of sodium chloride, for example. So the real value of TDS is as a warning of too many chemicals as a result of overloading or lack of dilution - and it should be monitored by comparison between pool and mains water. TDS should not be allowed to rise more than 1,000mg/l above source water, up to a maximum of 3,000mg/l. If TDS is high, and chloramines also, dilution is likely to be the answer.

The particular disinfectant used will affect TDS to some extent. Dosing to achieve 1mg/l of free chlorine using chlorine gas or sodium hypochlorite will increase TDS by about 1.7mg/l; calcium hypochlorite will increase TDS by 1.2mg/l. (This assumes that the acidic or alkaline nature of the disinfectants are neutralised.)

High TDS does not endanger the pool's water treatment, but does marginally encourage corrosion. Sulphates specifically can attack cement and grout. If, because of sodium bisulphate and aluminium sulphate (alum) use, sulphate levels cannot be kept below 360mg/l, sulphate-resistant Portland cement and epoxy grouts will be necessary to resist attack. Chloride can also corrode - see page 23.

Measuring TDS
The total dissolved solids (TDS) concentration of pool water is usually derived from the electrical conductivity of the water, measured by electronic meter. They either read TDS directly, or conductivity (conversion: conductivity in μS/cm x 0.7 = TDS in mg/l). Measurements should be taken weekly, following the manufacturer's instructions.

Sulphate concentration should be measured separately, because of its effect on cement and grout. There is a test kit for this, which should be used weekly at first, then - if results are satisfactory - every two months.

Controlling TDS
Dilution of the pool water by regular backwashing of filters is important in limiting the increase in concentration of these substances. It should be encouraged even though the operator may judge by the recorded head-loss that the filter does not need cleaning. The recommendation is to replace up to 30 litres of water per bather per day (see page 11). New methods including membrane filtration (reverse osmosis) are being developed which may provide ways of reducing TDS. Meanwhile, although dilution is usually the only practicable way to reduce TDS, using fewer chemicals and pre-swim showering may prevent its rising so high again.

WATER BALANCE

A balanced water is, technically, neither scale forming nor corrosive; that is, it shows no strong tendency to precipitate or to dissolve hardness salts. It is important to maintain the water in balance, but for most pools the water will be balanced if the pH is maintained within the recommended range. After pH value, the main factors which determine whether the water is balanced are alkalinity, hardness and dissolved solids. These are all to a large extent interrelated - but in a complex way. What is important is to make sure that a disinfectant appropriate to the source water is used; and that the nature of water balance is well understood.

Given a disinfectant appropriate to the source water, close attention to pH value, a check on alkalinity, and no obvious problems, water balance as an issue in itself is secondary. It becomes significant only when pH value and/or alkalinity vary from recommended values. To assess water balance formally, measurements are made of pH value, temperature, total alkalinity, calcium hardness and TDS. A simple formula or nomogram, depending on the particular index being determined, is then applied. The commonest index is Langelier - next page.

Langelier index

The Langelier index is calculated from factors (TF, CF and AF) derived respectively from the pool water temperature, calcium hardness and alkalinity - tabulated:

Temperature °C	TF		Calcium hardness as mg/l CaCO$_3$	CF		Alkalinity as mg/l CaCO$_3$	AF
24	0.6		75	1.5		50	1.7
29	0.7		100	1.6		100	2.0
			150	1.8		150	2.2
			200	1.9		200	2.3
			300	2.1		300	2.5
			400	2.3			
			800	2.5			

Langelier index = TF + CF + AF + pH value - 12.1
(The 12.1 figure assumes a total dissolved solids (TDS) figure below 1,000mg/l. If TDS are 2,000mg/l, the figure becomes 12.2; at 3,000mg/l, 12.3.)
In theory, a positive Langelier index indicates a scale-forming water; a negative indicates a corrosive water.

Water balance indices were not developed for the sort of water conditions found in swimming pools: following them slavishly can lead to over-use of chemicals. pH value has the greatest influence on index values, TDS least. The figures should be treated as ranges only - not as strict targets. A weekly index measurement will be enough - more than enough in most cases. Indices are indicative only, and no substitute for understanding and systematic maintenance of the various chemical levels.

MONITORING CHLORINE DISINFECTION

Regular testing of pool water is essential to ensure effective water treatment; it is the only satisfactory way of determining rapidly whether disinfection is adequate. Tests for disinfectant concentration should be carried out routinely. If the routine test results are outside the recommended ranges, the important thing is to establish what is happening, rather than rush into immediate action.

Frequency of testing
Disinfectant residuals (and pH values) should be checked manually by sampling the pool before it opens and after closing.

Beyond that, the frequency of testing depends upon the nature and use of the swimming pool. Many public pools now have instrumentation for the continuous monitoring of disinfectant residuals and pH values. This instrumentation is normally linked to the chemical dosing system, providing a more even treatment of the pool water and a closer control. Automatic monitors require checking daily, to ensure that the readings are correct. They do not mean that manual testing of water from the pool itself is unnecessary, although the frequency may be reduced - from every two hours for manual systems to perhaps three times a day with automatic systems.

In general, residual and pH value tests should be carried out at least three times a day on lightly-used pools; they may need to be done as often as once every two hours at a heavily-used pool. All such tests must be carried out immediately after the sample is taken.

At all pools it is necessary from time to time to test for other parameters. Some of these vary only slowly and so may be tested at weekly intervals - total dissolved solids, alkalinity, calcium hardness and sulphate concentration. Because water in a swimming pool is continuously recycled, an equilibrium is normally reached and test results stabilise so that the frequency of testing may be reduced. However the discipline of a weekly test is important. Some substances can be reduced only by dilution once they reach the limit of the recommended range - eg sulphate, total dissolved solids, bromide, cyanuric acid and dimethylhydantoin (DMH). This makes careful control essential. Simple test kits are available for these parameters (except DMH); manufacturers' instructions should be followed exactly.

Managing the monitoring

It is important that the test equipment is maintained and kept clean, and reagents subjected to regular quality control. All checks on the functioning of equipment, and results of water quality monitoring, must be recorded - see sample log sheet, page 121.

It is crucial that managers set up a foolproof system for acting on the results of monitoring. As a basis, all swimming pool operators should have full training to carry out tests on the water. Then there must be clear procedures for how they should act on any unexpected results - ideally, written down in a manual. Either operators must know what to do themselves, or know how to ensure that some appropriate action is taken by someone else. Many of the monitoring tests require the matching of colours, so operators should be examined for red/green colour blindness. The newer photometric kits (see page 85) eliminate some of these problems.

Management must monitor data and test systems regularly, and ensure that pool operator take appropriate remedial action.

Hypochlorites and chlorine gas

The disinfectant residual tests must determine both free chlorine (hypochlorous acid and hypochlorite ion) and combined chlorine (products of the reaction between ammonia and chlorine). They are generally performed with simple test kits based on the DPD method, using either liquid or tablet reagents. The manufacturer's instructions should be

followed - although the diagram on this page illustrates a variation that PWTAG recommends to ensure no contamination.

The reactions between chlorine and ammoniacal compounds in the pool are complex (see page 38 for more detail) and it is dangerous to over-simplify the meaning of test results.

But free chlorine should be as low as is consistent with satisfactory microbiological quality - less than 1mg/l in a well designed and run pool (see page 39). The combined chlorine residual should be no more than half the free - certainly less than 1mg/l where the pool water treatment is operating well. If it exceeds this, and DPD reagents indicate the presence of monochloramines, then the chlorine dose should be checked, to make sure it is at the right level. (If it is, then the chances are there is too much ammonia, so bathing loads or pollution from bathers may be too high.)

Monochloramine and dichloramine should be brought under control in an hour or so by breakpoint chlorination (see page 38). Although this is complicated by the slow formation of ammonia from the breakdown of urea, by the recycling nature of the swimming pool water, and increased pool loading, it should be possible to follow the ratios of combined to free chlorine and draw conclusions accordingly. For example, if maintaining the correct level of chlorination reduces chloramines, the pool water is satisfactory. If increasing free chlorine also increases the combined chlorine, the pool water is unsatisfactory.

If the combined chlorine is over 1mg/l, but monochloramine levels are low, then organic

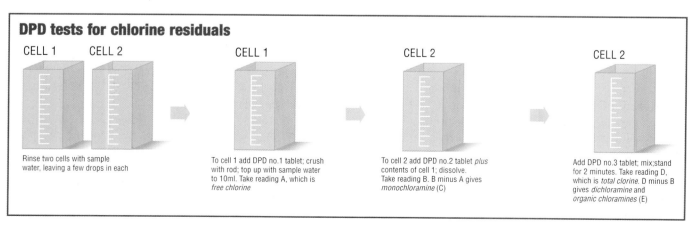

DPD tests for chlorine residuals

CELL 1   CELL 2

Rinse two cells with sample water, leaving a few drops in each

CELL 1

To cell 1 add DPD no.1 tablet; crush with rod; top up with sample water to 10ml. Take reading A, which is *free chlorine*

CELL 2

To cell 2 add DPD no.2 tablet *plus* contents of cell 1; dissolve. Take reading B. B minus A gives *monochloramine* (C)

CELL 2

Add DPD no.3 tablet; mix;stand for 2 minutes. Take reading D, which is *total clorine*. D minus B gives *dichloramine* and *organic chloramines* (E)

chloramines must be present (see page 39); in this case the pool water should be diluted by replacing some of it with fresh make-up water.

Any explanation or advice given on one set of results may be unsatisfactory as much depends on trends within the system. A build up of organic chlorine residuals is the normal cause of difficulty. So these readings need to be watched to ensure that there is not a gradual increase over a period of days or weeks. If there is a persistent problem of this sort, the basic operation of the pool may be flawed. The calculations described at the beginning of Chapter 2 should be checked: bathing load or turnover period may have to be reduced.

Testing regime   Many modern pools have multiple outlets and inlets; samples should be taken at various parts of the pool, at a depth of 300mm, to select a point which is typical of the general concentration in the pool. It is good practice to include as a routine sampling point the area of the pool where, because of the hydraulics, the disinfectant residual is the lowest in the pool. Occasional samples should be taken from other parts of the pool and circulation system.

There are several areas in testing for chlorine residuals that cause problems. If the tube and cap from the previous colour test have been used for total chlorine and are not thoroughly rinsed, subsequent tests for free chlorine may give false, high readings. A calcium hardness of over 500mg/l as $CaCO_3$ may also give false, high readings, although some brands of DPD tablets will cope with hardness up to 1,000mg/l. The DPD colour may be bleached by high (normally over 10mg/l) chlorine residuals and thus give false low readings. If this is suspected, the test should be repeated on a sample diluted 1:1 with distilled water (before taking any remedial action). The DPD No 1 test should in any case begin with only 1-2 drops of pool water, so that any bleaching out (a flash of colour, then nothing) is clearly identified.

Acting on chlorine residual results   The data arising from testing chlorine residuals in pools disinfected with hypochlorite or chlorine gas can be used to improve water quality and management. Pools with high combined chlorine (but satisfactory free chlorine) in the morning before bathers enter need more dilution or a lower bathing load - assuming

nothing else has gone wrong, for example with the overnight dosing. The type of inorganic combined chlorine present in the water will depend upon the pH value. The nuisance, irritant residuals are more stable at low pH values and the comments given here assume that the pH value is correct (see page 78). If the pool demonstrates objectionable chlorinous odours it is more likely that the pH is too low and this should be checked immediately.

The recommended chlorine residual levels are given in Chapter 6. Rules of thumb are repeated here for action on test results. The free chlorine residual in a decent pool might be 1mg/l (0.5mg/l if it has ozone). Free chlorine residuals above 2mg/l should not be necessary anywhere in the pool unless the circulation is too slow, the distribution poor or bathing loads too heavy. A chlorine residual above 3mg/l is unlikely to be necessary: chlorination should be reduced. Above 5mg/l free chlorine, chlorination should be stopped immediately and above 10mg/l bathing should cease. The same applies to pools on chloroisocyanurates, except that chlorine residuals of up to 5mg/l may be necessary in normal operation.

If pool water or atmospheric conditions become uncomfortable at lower residuals, this should be investigated and dealt with.

Dechlorination

If it is necessary to reduce chlorine residual in a pool because of accidental overtreatment (or for a dye test), sodium thiosulphate or hydrogen peroxide can be used. (If the combined chlorine is also high, dumping water is probably a better device.) Peroxide has the advantage that it is a good oxidiser, has some disinfectant potential and breaks down harmlessly to oxygen and water (though it is more hazardous to handle). Thiosulphate can cause cloudiness and raise sulphate levels.

The amounts used are based on the free chlorine residual and the pool volume. If the free chlorine is 1mg/l and the pool volume is 487m³, there will be 487g of chlorine
- @ 2g sodium thiosulphate per 1g of chlorine, about 2kg would be needed for dechlorination
- @ 1.5ml of 30% hydrogen peroxide per 1g of chlorine, about 750ml would be needed.

The quantity to be added should be mixed into a watering can of water and poured over the surface of the pool (obviously with no bathers present). The pool should then have one turnover period before bathers are allowed to return - after checking that the chlorine residual is satisfactory.

AUTOMATIC MONITORING

Automatic monitoring and control equipment for disinfectant residuals and pH value is widely used to provide optimum treatment, particularly in heavily loaded pools. These monitors are generally more accurate than test kits, although they are normally calibrated (carefully, by a skilled operator) using such a kit. The calibration sample is the same water as that which the analyser samples. So readings from the pool will not necessarily be the same as those given by the analyser. What matters is that there is a consistent and understood relationship between the two.

It is extremely important that the monitoring and control equipment receives samples that are representative of water quality generally and thus will ensure optimum values throughout the pool. The better the water is distributed, the easier this is. It is equally important that such instrumentation is checked by taking a sample at the unit about twice a week for accuracy using the appropriate tests.

Modern controllers have automatic or semi-automatic calibration features but, as with all instrumentation, careful calibration and maintenance by fully trained operators are essential for accurate results.

Automatic monitoring is dealt with in the context of automatic dosing control in general in Chapter 10.

Sensors

There are two types of sensor used to measure and thus control pool water disinfectant parameters - amperometric and redox.

Amperometric These chlorine residual analysers are widely used for measurement and control. They generally measure hypochlorous acid (free chlorine residual comprises both hypochlorous acid and hypochlorite ion). In calibrating such sensors it is important that the pH value of the water is constant (unless a buffer solution is added to the sample stream to the analyser). Only in this way can the DPD test be used to calibrate the amperometric sensor. Testing of automatic analysers should be carried out on the sample used for the analyser and not, say, from the pool itself. These analysers should be adjusted only if there is a significant discrepancy in the chlorine readings and a constant pH value since the last calibration. If cyanuric acid or bromine-based disinfectants are used, the amperometric analyser must be able to measure them and be calibrated accordingly.

Redox These analysers measure simply the oxidative power of pool water. So they give only a qualitative estimate of free chlorine - a useful indication of how water quality is affected by bather pollution. Control of chlorine residuals is coarser than with amperometric, as redox controllers do not react so readily to small changes in chlorine residual level - particularly with high levels.

Redox control levels should be set so as to effect a satisfactory chlorine residual during and just after heavy bathing load conditions. This will ensure sufficient residual at other times. Calibration of the analyser against redox test solutions (not DPD) is important to ensure that the redox value (in millivolts) is accurate and can be sensibly interpreted and compared to the actual chlorine residuals in the swimming pool. Manual testing of the pool water for free chlorine remains important.

Redox monitors are frequently used on their own to control pool water chlorination. They can be used to indicate the presence of ozone. They can also be used alongside amperometric analysers: they provide the warning of water quality deterioration - while amperometric analysers control the free chlorine residual.

pH value

Automatic testing for pH value is normally done on the sample taken for the disinfectant residual. Calibration of the pH electrodes (probes) against buffer solutions - reagents of known pH value - should be done weekly (but

pH and chlorine sensors and controllers at a multi-pool complex

the relationship of pH value with chlorine residual results should be constantly evaluated) and the pH electrodes should show a good response to changes in pH value. Some pH buffers absorb CO_2 and change their characteristics - so they must be fresh and uncontaminated to be free of discrepancies.

Even good quality glass electrodes (more expensive, usually) have a limited life - handled properly, about a year.

Photometer readings will show small variations from those of the automatic analyser with some waters - but anything more than 0.2mg/l should be investigated.

MAINTAINING WATER QUALITY

The disinfectant residual, pH value and other chemical parameters for particular systems should be maintained within the specified levels described throughout this book. If the operational hints given in this chapter are followed, there should be adequate disinfection of the water and good swimming conditions, provided filtration and circulation are adequate. It is not sensible to give more exact figures than have been given, as the control of treatment plant aims to maintain good disinfection, water balance and clarity by the minimum use of treatment chemicals. Where consistently good water quality can be achieved by relaxing some of the stated figures, this is acceptable and will often give optimum swimming conditions - but should be done only with a good understanding of the particular system.

Steady, satisfactory chemical parameters are best maintained if water conditions are stabilised by regular backwashing and the addition of fresh dilution water. The resulting reduction in the levels of total dissolved solids, bather pollution and combined chlorine residual help achieve good test results and - the final test - provide better bather comfort.

TEST KITS

As far as choosing a test kit is concerned, it is unwise to begrudge the relatively small difference in price between a good kit and one that may be untried. In use, there are nine important points to avoid inaccuracies.

- Test kits must be kept scrupulously clean at all times. This applies especially to glassware for colour matching or light transmitting tests. The glassware should be thoroughly rinsed with tap water, or preferably distilled (deionised) water, so that all traces of test reagents are removed before making any subsequent tests.
- The shelf life of the reagents must not be exceeded. Liquid reagents need to be replaced at regular intervals to ensure that they remain active; when not in use, the bottles must be adequately stoppered or closed; tablet reagents must be stored in a cool dry place. For maximum shelf life, all tablets are available individually packed in foil strips.
- Using the right tablets (specified by the manufacturer) for the particular instrument is imperative.
- If the test develops sludge or bubbles, it should be left for a few minutes: if the reading falls, the wrong tablet may have been used.
- Buying tablets in bulk is clearly attractive financially - and makes sense where a number of pools in the same authority have the same kits. But if any of the test kits are different, results will be unreliable. Care must be taken over shelf life.
- When testing for halogen residuals, any colour in the sample that is at or beyond the top or bottom concentration shown on the test kit cannot be assumed or guessed. Only colour matching within the range of the disc can have the accuracy of the test method. If the reading is at the bottom, the result should be recorded as less than the range; if at the top or beyond, the test can be repeated with a dilute sample (not for pH value).
- Operators, who must not be colour blind, should be trained in the use of test kits (including the importance of a good light source) to ensure accurate results. A photometer overcomes the problem of colour blindness.
- Photometric measuring systems eliminate colour matching. Photometers take an absorbence reading of the test solution and convert it into a digital readout in mg/l.
- Pool cleaning chemicals can interfere with results.

Testing test kits
Over the years, there has been some doubt about the reliability of test kits. PWTAG

responded with some direct research. Two comparator and two photometer kits (from different manufacturers) were tested by an experienced analytical laboratory. Each of the four was used at three swimming pools; then pool water was taken to the laboratory where it was re-tested with the four kits and against standard methods of analysis.

The research findings were reassuring. The four test kits were considered robust and fit for purpose for pH value and for free and total chlorine measurements. The more expensive photometer kits were more discriminating, and less affected by turbidity. In general, however, interference from normal levels of pool contaminants was not significant.

Their accuracy was compared to results from standard laboratory methods. Their precision was plus or minus:
- 0.1 pH unit
- 0.08-0.12mg/l free chlorine
- 0.14-0.18mg/l total chlorine.

In practice The significance of these accuracy figures is that they make it realistic to use test kits as aids in refining pool water treatment in the pursuit of lower chlorine residuals.

It is important that a pool's chlorine residual targets be based on a thorough understanding of all aspects of the pool's operation. The desire to offer a more comfortable swim must be tempered by the necessity to provide a safe one. But the lower figures represent the ideal for bathers and staff, and should be the target for pool operators managers. Higher residuals certainly shouldn't be used just to compensate for bad management practices.

The chart here demonstrates how these principles can be applied in a systematic way to explore the possibility of improving water quality by reducing free chlorine.

Pool improvement

Are daily pool-side tests done (and records kept) by trained operators, in line with this book? — NO → Ensure that the management system introduces routine testing and recording

YES ↓

Do free chlorine levels conform with those planned for the pool; are combined chlorine and pH in line with this book? — NO → Check that the pool is operating within the limits of its design – eg bathing load, filtration rate, dilution (see Chapter 3)

↓ All OK after corrective action (if not OK get advice)

YES ↓

Are other (non-daily) tests, including microbiology, done as often as this book recommends? — NO → Ensure management system includes these tests and arrange for them to happen

YES ↓

Are all routine tests now meeting the standards of this book? — NO

YES ↓

Does the pool treatment design and management meet all the standards in this book? — NO → Carry on operating at current free chlorine residual

↓ OR

If you still wish to reduce the free chlorine residual, seek specialist advice

YES ↓

It may be possible to reduce the free chlorine residual level – by, say, 0.2mg/l steps - continuing chemical and microbiological testing as usual. Be prepared to adjust upwards again at times of peak loading; and make sure the plant has the capacity for this

Chapter 14

Healthy swimming

For historical, cultural and emotional or psychological reasons, swimming is for many the epitome of health - the perfect exercise in the most natural medium. And the ability to swim is the basis of confident, safe participation in a wide variety of other aquatic recreations. The recreational side of swimming, and the health considerations of swimming in natural waters, PWTAG leaves for others to pronounce on. But the water in swimming pools, and the air above them, are very much PWTAG's concern; its number one priority has always been the comfort and safety of bathers. Were pool water ever to be poor enough to cancel out the benefits of the exercise, swimming would not be healthy.

There are broadly two ways this might happen. The nastier byproducts of water treatment - chloramines, trihalomethanes and the rest - might cause ill health. It is always difficult to be sure about the effects of long-term but very low-level exposure to potentially harmful agents. This is discussed in detail at the end of this chapter (page 94), and the implications for pool water management are spelt out wherever relevant throughout the book. The overall message is that, although we must continually sharpen our scientific and medical focus on this (and, of course, maintain the highest standards in pools), there is no good evidence that there is a health problem. But given that, however carefully pool waters are managed, some potentially harmful byproducts are bound to enter the air, good ventilation (Chapter 19) becomes very important.

The second route to possible ill-health would be infection and other illness caused directly by the water. That means germs mainly, and the effects of disinfectants. Bathers are more alert to this than they once were, and likely to be increasingly keen to assert their consumer right to a healthy swim. Luckily, it can be said with confidence that swimming pools present no special risk of illness provided they are properly managed and disinfected.

This chapter deals with infections, the occasionally harmful effects of swimming in disinfected water, advice about the circumstances under which people should consider not going swimming, and the health effects of disinfection byproducts.

INFECTIONS

Lots of infections have been linked in the public perception with swimming pools. Many are simply impossible. Pool operators should know about these, so that they can give instant, confident reassurance should their threat be raised.

The first category of empty threats are those infections which are spread person to person, not through water. These include:

- polio - in any case, caused by a virus no longer found in Western Europe
- sexually transmitted diseases, hepatitis B and HIV - but see Blood spillages on page 91
- meningococcal meningitis.

Those microorganisms whose infections *can* be waterborne are listed alphabetically in the table on page 88. The empty threats here (printed in black) are those which have not caused infections in swimming pools, for the reasons listed in the table. They include:

- *Escherichia coli*
- *Legionella* - but see page 92
- *Leptospira*
- Swimmer's itch.

So, again, pool operators can be reassuring about these.

Those organisms printed red in the table have caused infections in swimming pools and are dealt with in detail in this chapter. Even with those, recorded incidents are rare. For example *Cryptosporidium*, perhaps the commonest, is associated with only one or two outbreaks a year in the UK. In most cases infections have been linked to failures in the pool's water

Waterborne infections

Acanthamoeba	Amoebae readily isolated from bathing waters and have caused rare infections linked to spa pools. Can contaminate contact lenses and cause ulcers
Adenoviruses	Viruses causing pharyngoconjunctival fever in inadequately disinfected pools
Cryptosporidium parvum	Protozoa, the commonest cause of diarrhoea in pools. Resistant to chlorine but not to filtration
Dermatophyte fungi	Athlete's foot from surfaces contaminated by fungi
Escherichia coli (E coli)	Bacteria spread mainly through food (eg type 0157) and person to person. One outbreak resulted from an inadequately disinfected paddling pool. Killed by chlorine
Giardia lamblia	Protozoa similar (including effect) to *Cryptosporidium parvum*
Hepatitis A virus	Infectious hepatitis spread through contaminated food and water; killed by chlorine
Legionella pneumophila	Respiratory infection spread by bacteria in sprays - can be a problem in spas. Killed by chlorine
Leptospira	Bacteria from urine of infected rats etc; cause Weil's disease in rivers and lakes; killed by chlorine
Mycobacterium marinum	Bacteria occasionally found in pools; causes a very rare skin condition - granuloma. Killed by chlorine
Naegleria fowleri	Amoebae which can cause meningitis; found in thermal spring water but not a problem with mains water; in any case, killed by chlorine
Papilloma virus	Plantar warts (verrucas) caused by contact with contaminated surfaces
Pseudomonas aeruginosa	A bacteria affecting mainly spa pools, occasionally swimming pools; heavy contamination of badly run pools can cause folliculitis and ear infections; killed by chlorine
Shigella	Bacteria causing dysentery, occasionally in badly run pools; killed by chlorine
Trichobilharzia, Schistosoma	Flatworm causing swimmers' itch - but only in waters containing snails

Only those organisms printed in red have caused infection in swimming pools

management. It can certainly be said, once again, that a well run pool should be adequate protection against infection. The following pages assess the few real possibilities of illness and describe how they may be minimised. There is an important section (next page) on measures to cope with the threat and the reality of defaecation in the pool.

TRANSMISSION OF INFECTION

The number of pathogens likely to be present in pool water is so small that the risk of bather infection is very slight. Such infections are more likely to be spread in other ways. Wherever people congregate - at work, in shops, in theatres, on public transport, etc - there are opportunities for pathogens to be spread by personal contact or in the air. Crowded pools and changing areas are no exception. So overcrowding should be avoided; and pool surrounds, changing rooms, toilets, etc should be kept clean and hygienic. If disinfection is inadequate, or if hygiene standards are not maintained, it is possible for certain infections to be transmitted by the pool water. Bathers themselves, of course, have a responsibility to follow basic rules of hygiene, which should be reinforced through health education.

GASTRO-INTESTINAL INFECTIONS

In a well managed and adequately disinfected pool, most microorganisms responsible for gastro-intestinal infections and diarrhoea (*Shigella*, for example), if introduced into the water, will be inactivated by dilution in the large volume of pool water and by the disinfectant residual. But there are two problem organisms.

Cryptosporidium and *Giardia* are microscopic protozoa (unicellular organisms) found throughout the environment, often in animals. They can cause diarrhoeal illness. Because their infectious stages - oocyst and cyst respectively - are relatively resistant to chlorine disinfectants, they can be a problem in pools. But the cysts are larger than bacteria and therefore more susceptible to coagulation and filtration.

So pool operators must be aware of the risks involved in faecal release into pools.

Faecal release into pools

Because of the risks involved, a pool operator faced with a release of faeces into the pool must decide on an appropriate course of action very quickly. If the operator gets it wrong, there is a chance that significant numbers of bathers might become ill.

If the release is a solid stool, it should simply be retrieved quickly and the scoop disinfected. As long as the pool is in other respects operating properly (disinfectant residuals, etc) no further action is necessary. The same applies to solid animal faeces.

If the stool is runny (diarrhoea) the pool should be cleared of bathers immediately. If the incident has happened in a small pool (for children, say) the safest action is to empty and clean it before refilling and reopening. If this is not practicable, the choice is more difficult.

The likeliest cause of the diarrhoea is a virus or bacterium that is susceptible to disinfection. A child with diarrhoea might introduce billions of infective particles into the water, and the infective dose can be as low as one particle. But although there is an immediate risk, the bugs should be inactivated within a matter of minutes by disinfection. Operators would, however, have to run the pool at the top of its disinfectant residual range for, say, 15 minutes, during which time all parts of the pool should be checked for chlorine residual. Only then would bathers be allowed back into the pool.

The other possibility, however, is that the diarrhoea is from someone infected with one of the protozoal parasites, *Cryptosporidium* and *Giardia*. They are a problem for swimming pools because their infectious stages are resistant to chlorine disinfectants. So the procedure just described would be inadequate.

The appropriate procedure relies on the fact that the cysts are, in principle, large enough to be filtered out.

- The pool is cleared of people immediately.
- Disinfectant levels are maintained at the top of the recommended range.
- The pool is vacuumed and swept.
- Using a coagulant, the water is filtered for six turnover cycles (which could well take up to a day, and so might mean closing the pool until the next day).
- The filter is backwashed.
- The pool can then be reopened.

Clearly this is a fairly drastic course of action that any pool operator would want to avoid if possible. But if there is good reason to suspect that *Cryptosporidium* or *Giardia* is responsible (certainly if the person involved has had diarrhoea for some days), it would be the safest procedure. The local consultant in communicable disease control (CCDC) should be notified. A copy of such emergency measures can usefully be included in the operation and maintenance manual.

Even so, however, there is some doubt about the ability of pool filters to do the job well enough to deal with the millions of cysts produced in such an incident - a few of which can be enough to infect someone. And in any case pool operators are unlikely to know what has caused a diarrhoea incident. Finally, a significant proportion of such diarrhoea incidents - perhaps the majority - will happen without pool attendants being aware of it.

So the most important contribution a pool operator can make to the problem is to guard against it.

Keeping diarrhoea out of the pool

There are a few practical actions pool operators can take to help prevent faecal release into pools.

- Children under the age of six months can be discouraged from swimming in public pools, where they may in any case find the temperatures and chemicals irritate their sensitive skin. An ordinary bath can be a better start.
- When children do start to swim it should not be in nappies, but in special baby swimming trunks. There should be good nappy-changing facilities.
- Parents should be educated (by posters, for example) about the risk. It should be made very clear that no child (or adult) with a recent history of diarrhoea should swim.
- Parents should be encouraged to make sure their children use the toilet before they swim
- Thorough pre-swim showering is a good idea and parents should encourage their children to do it - preferably by example. At the other end of the spectrum, washing babies' bottoms in the pool is a bad idea.
- It may be worth confining young children to pools small enough to drain in the event of such an accident.

FOOT INFECTIONS

The chance of transmitting a foot infection can be reduced by keeping floors clean - see page 126. The limited role of footbaths in controlling foot infections is dealt with on page 29.

Athlete's foot (tinea pedis) is a ringworm infection caused by dermatophyte fungi which causes itchy scale between the toes. It can be acquired during visits to swimming pools, spread by contact with floor surfaces contaminated by skin fragments infected with the fungus. Floor cleaning reduces the number of the infective particles. People with severe athlete's foot should not attend swimming pools. However, it is not realistic to exclude those with possible infection between the toes, as it is difficult to distinguish between infection and soggy skin. Attempting to exclude children is particularly futile, as athlete's foot is unusual in children.

Verrucas (plantar warts) can be acquired through contact with floor surfaces contaminated by skin fragments infected with the causative papillomavirus. Historically, efforts have been made to exclude verruca sufferers from swimming pools in the hope that the spread of the virus could be reduced. However, verrucas are common, and there are undoubtedly other means by which the virus is spread. There is a substantial body of medical opinion which considers that exclusion cannot be justified. Immunity to infection appears to develop readily, as verrucas are uncommon in adults, including those who participate regularly in barefoot activities. It is very doubtful if a firm exclusion policy influences the incidence of verrucas, and it is difficult to implement as well as distressing to children.

EYE IRRITATION

High levels of free chlorine residual, even at the top of the recommended range, are not normally what cause eye irritation in pools. It is usually due to byproducts of the reactions between disinfectant and pollutants. So irritation is likely to be reduced by any measures that lower the combined chlorine residual, such as minimising contamination, operating with lower free chlorine residuals, generous routine dilution with fresh water, or the use of ozone or UV.

pH values outside the recommended range are also a factor in eye irritation, as may be other pool chemicals (especially alum if incorrectly used - see page 75). Dosing via skimmer baskets, and slug dosing, may also increase the chances of eye irritation.

Conjunctivitis (inflammation of the eye) may appear during visits to pools, but is rarely due to infection at all. Conjunctivitis may result from prolonged immersion - especially if the eyes are kept open - because of the difference in the concentration of various salts between the fluid of the eye and pool water. It is worsened by high combined chlorine levels.

Where there is bacterial or viral eye infection, it is likely to have come, not from pool water, but from close contact with infected people, or infected articles such as towels. Irritation of the eye by pool water does, however, make picking up such an infection more likely. Pharyngo-conjunctival fever is dealt with under Viruses below.

People who wear soft contact lenses can, unusually, get ulcers on their cornea. This is usually caused by trauma to the eye or using dirty contact lens fluid, even tap water. But the organism involved - *Acanthamoeba* - can be found in pool water (spas particularly) and its cysts are resistant to chlorine. If bathers cannot swim without their soft lenses (or wear goggles), they should remove them afterwards and clean them with lens fluid.

VIRUSES

Viral infections are not spread in well-managed and adequately disinfected pools. Nevertheless, some viruses, including the adenoviruses that cause pharyngo-conjunctival fever (which affects nose and eyes), have been isolated from pools with too little disinfectant. However, naso-pharyngeal and respiratory infections are usually spread by infected airborne droplets; bathers are more likely to contract these diseases in crowded areas than through contact with the pool water. Nose and sinus problems may also result from changes in osmotic pressure, or chemical irritation.

Hepatitis and HIV
Hepatitis A is normally transmitted in food and water, and its spread in a pool is, like gastro-intestinal infections, very unlikely.

Hepatitis B virus and the human immunodeficiency virus (HIV) are carried in blood and other body fluids. Infections are transmitted by inoculation into body tissue - by sexual intercourse, injection, cuts, etc. The viruses are susceptible to the action of disinfectant and neither condition has ever been known to be spread as the result of using a swimming pool.

Because HIV and hepatitis B viruses can be blood-borne, however, blood spillages should be taken seriously wherever they occur - including pools.

Blood spillage If substantial amounts of blood (or vomit) are spilled into the pool, it should be temporarily cleared of people, to allow the pollution to disperse and any infective particles within it to be neutralised by the disinfectant in the water. Operators should confirm that disinfectant residuals and pH values are within the recommended ranges.

Any blood spillage on the poolside should not be washed into the pool or poolside drains. Instead, like blood spillage anywhere in the building, it should be dealt with using strong disinfectant - of a concentration equivalent to 10,000mg/l of available chlorine; a 1% solution of hypochlorite may be convenient. The blood should be covered with paper towels, gently flooded with the disinfectant and left for at least two minutes before it is cleared away. On the poolside, the affected area can then be washed with pool water. Elsewhere, the area should be washed with water and detergent and, if possible, left to dry. The person clearing up the spillage will need to wear gloves. The bagged paper towels and gloves should, if possible, be incinerated.

SKIN

Skin irritation and rashes can be linked to swimming pools. It is a complicated subject, and it is difficult to be sure how far a rash is due to the water (and its disinfectant), how far it is due to other factors in the sufferer's physical makeup and environment. But the relevant government committee (see page 101) recommended that all pool operators are vigilant about the issue. The most important safeguard against such skin problems is good water management and adequate dilution.

Skin rashes associated with pools are mainly due to one or more of the following factors:

- wetting and degreasing - especially with warm water and prolonged exposure
- degreasing - with most disinfectants
- chemical irritation - usually trivial in chlorinated pools but more from pools using bromochlorodimethylhydantoin (BCDMH).
- infection - which rarely cause rashes in swimming pools but may do so in whirlpool spas (see below).

These four factors contribute to the three commonest skin conditions - new pool rash, bromine itch and folliculitis.

New pool rash and holidaymaker's rash
These are usually described by sufferers as 'dry skin' and are characteristic of bathers unused to prolonged swimming. Bathing for an hour or two in warm pool water can produce a rash. Most are mild dermatitis, and respond well to emollient creams and/or reducing exposure.

Bromine itch
This is associated with the use of BCDMH, which for some people in some pools produces an intensely itching contact dermatitis (ie eczema) especially after re-exposure. The itching usually precedes a visible rash within 12 hours of exposure. The frequency of the rash increases with age, being unusual in children and more common in bathers of more than 50 years of age. It is also more frequent and severe with prolonged exposure, which may occur occupationally - for example, to hydrotherapists. The Bibliography (page 138) lists papers on the subject (and see page 33).

The distinction between bromine itch and folliculitis (next section) is not difficult:

- the chemical irritation of bromine itch invariably appears within 12 hours of exposure; folliculitis usually takes at least 24 hours to become consolidated
- itching, sometimes severe, is the main symptom of bromine rash and is minimal with folliculitis
- for those who are susceptible, bromine itch continues in a pool with levels of disinfectant which are incompatible with large numbers of pathogenic pseudomonads.

Folliculitis

This is due to infection of skin hair follicles with the pathogenic bacterium, *Pseudomonas aeruginosa*. A combination of intense skin wetting and high concentrations of pseudomonads in the pool water are necessary conditions for this complaint. These factors usually appear only in spas via prolonged exposure (1or 2 hours) to very warm water (over 32°C) and with disinfection failure, thus allowing heavy bacterial growth within the water treatment system. It has been linked also to swimming pools, but less commonly.

As the next chapter describes, routine testing for *Ps aeruginosa* is not recommended. But if high levels are found there is no need for a shutdown. Instead: check water clarity; check residuals and pH; resample; backwash thoroughly; wait one turnover; resample.

Swimming pool granuloma

Mycobacterium marinum is a relatively chlorine-resistant bacterium that can occasionally grow in warm swimming pools and tropical aquaria. It can infect skin rubbed by rough surfaces - worn grout or rough tiling, for example. Swimming pool granuloma is rare.

EAR AND SINUS INFECTIONS

Swimmer's ear (otitis externa) is caused by wetting, dewaxing and degreasing of the outer ear. This may result in itching eczema (due to skin damage) with or without infection, which is usually by the sort of bacteria which are almost always present even on healthy skin. High numbers of pathogenic *Pseudomonas aeruginosa* in a swimming pool - due to inadequate disinfection - may cause an unusually high incidence of swimmer's ear. It is likeliest in distance and competitive swimmers.

Infection of the middle ear (otitis media) and sinusitis, if they follow swimming, are most likely to have been caused by infected mucus forced into the naso-pharyngeal tubes while swimming.

MENINGITIS

Most forms of meningitis cannot be transmitted through swimming. *Naegleria fowleri* is a pathogenic, free-living amoeba and a very rare cause of meningitis associated with swimming. In every case the pool has been found to be receiving polluted, warm spring water - and to be inadequately disinfected. Pool make-up water must be clean and come from secure sources. Circulation systems, including balance tanks, should be designed to avoid long periods of stagnation; debris should be removed regularly.

LEGIONNAIRES' DISEASE

This severe form of pneumonia is caused by the *Legionella pneumophila* bacterium. But for it to be spread, contaminated water must form a spray (technically, an aerosol) that can be inhaled. Infections are typically from spray humidifiers or cooling towers. No case of Legionnaires' disease (legionellosis) has ever been associated with conventional swimming pools.

Poorly managed spa pools can, however, become infected and spread the disease, through the fine spray generated at the turbulent water surface. Careful maintenance, frequent filter backwashing and close attention to disinfectant levels are critical. This applies even to spas operating only for display. Showers, too, are a potential source of infected spray. Supply water should be stored above 60°C and piped at 50°C or more to prevent the survival and growth of legionella.

Pool water features with spray effects - rain sprays, fountains, etc - should be checked, the heads cleaned and periodically flushed with 5-10mg/l chlorine. Showers, too, should be checked.

Details about control are in the Health & Safety Executive booklet, *The control of legionellosis* (see Bibliography).

RESPIRATORY COMPLAINTS

Warm, humid air in a pool hall should be particularly comfortable for people with respiratory problems like coughs, sinusitis and even asthma. Some asthmatics, however, have to be wary of any exercise; they may need to take medicine before swimming. And swimmers in training squads may be affected by wheeziness, etc.

Asthma attacks are triggered either by the specific substance to which the person is allergic, eg pollen; or by larger amounts of any irritant in the air. Chloramines and other substances in pool hall air can bring on an attack in someone already asthmatic; but they do not in themselves cause asthma. People do not seem to become allergic to pool hall contaminants.

The same applies to what is called maturity onset asthma - asthma appearing in middle age, sometimes for the first time. Occasionally its appearance is blamed, wrongly, on pool conditions; in fact, other, complex factors are responsible.

Nevertheless, high combined chlorines - especially if nitrogen trichloride is involved - can cause respiratory discomfort. Prolonged, frequent exposure of people bathing or working in such atmospheres can cause a number of eye, throat and chest symptoms that almost mimic flu. The answer is simply to avoid the high chloramine levels that come with poor design, over-loading and bad management. It is now possible to measure chloramines, including nitrogen trichloride, in the air and specify levels above which problems are more likely. A safety level for nitrogen trichloride in the air of 0.1ppm (about 0.5mg/m^3) has been proposed.

In any case all public pools need an effective ventilation system which removes irritants from above the water and expels them. Ventilation systems that rely on recirculating air tend to build up these irritants. See Chapter 19.

The fact that disinfection by-products affect respiratory complaints should be included in COSHH assessments (see page 119).

When not to swim

A swimming pool is not very different from any other public place. Just as people might avoid work, school or public transport when they are not well - for their own sake as much as for others - so there are circumstances when swimming might be avoided.

- Children under the age of six months may find the temperatures and chemicals in pools unwelcome because of their sensitive skin.
- When children do start swimming, it should not be in nappies: there are special baby costumes.
- Parents should make sure that children go to the toilet before swimming. Everyone would be doing the pool a favour if they showered - preferaby nude, and making sure heads, armpits, genitals, backsides and feet are clean - before bathing.
- Swimming on a full stomach is still a bad idea because of cramp.
- People should not bathe if they have open wounds, severe eczema or any other infectious skin complaint.
- Colds, flu and other infectious illnesses are a sufficient reason not to swim; so is diarrhoea within the previous two weeks.
- Ideally, people with head lice, athlete's foot or verrucas should not go to public pools.
- People whose illness or treatment makes them susceptible to infection, or affected badly by it, should take medical advice before swimming.
- People should not swim if they are affected by drink or drugs.

Pool managers must decide for themselves how to pass on messages like these. A policy of exclusion is not really enforceable - but there is no harm in gently but firmly letting people know what their responsibilities are.

HEALTH EFFECTS OF DISINFECTION BYPRODUCTS

In practice, health considerations may never contribute significantly to the choice of disinfectant for a particular pool. It is generally accepted, as it is for drinking water, that disinfection should not be compromised by anxiety about the sometimes theoretical risks from chemical byproducts. And only the halamines (chloramines and bromamines) discussed below are included in routine pool water testing. But it is important that pool managers and operators know something of the health issues that underpin the way disinfectants are used (and may be abused) - in particular, the significance of the different byproducts of disinfection. At the very least it gives them something specific to say to people concerned about health issues.

This section reviews what is known about the significance of different levels of these byproducts. Throughout, it is almost impossible to be specific about the safety of different concentrations - partly because it is not known for sure how much water is ingested while swimming, and how much of the different byproducts find their way into body tissues. This will anyway be affected by the intensity and length of the swim.

In many cases, an indication of what line pool operators might follow can be taken from drinking water standards. In the UK these are set by the relevant environment departments and are based on the European Community Drinking Water Directives. There are also references in this section to the World Health Organisation (WHO). Its latest *Guidelines for Drinking Water* were published in November 1993 (see Bibliography). A new Drinking Water Directive has been published, with many of its standards based on WHO guidelines. The UK will be implementing these standards through new regulations.

Chloramines

Chloramines appear in swimming pools (see page 38) as a result of the reaction between ammonia compounds (especially from urine and sweat) and chlorine-based disinfectants. There are no UK standards for chloramines in drinking water - although it is used by some water companies as a disinfectant (see page 10). WHO recommends a guideline value of 3mg/l for monochloramine, but it has not recommended values for di or trichloramine because there are not enough toxicity data.

Chloramines contribute to combined chlorine residuals in pool water, and are responsible for most of the so-called 'chlorine smell' and eye irritation associated with badly-run pools. This book recommends keeping the combined chlorine residual as low as 0.5mg/l (see page 39). Page 83 details the remedial action to be taken if levels rise excessively.

Bromamines

Like chloramines, bromamines arise from reactions between nitrogenous matter and bromine-based disinfectants. Bromamines are not expected to be present in drinking water (as bromine products are rarely used for its disinfection), so there are no standards there.

In pools, their presence is undesirable for much the same reasons as chloramines. Nevertheless, because monobromamine does have significant disinfectant properties (unlike monochloramine), operators using bromine-based disinfectants often have targets for total bromine residual. Ideally, they should check on the combined bromine levels too, and take action if either becomes excessive (see page 43).

Trihalomethanes (THMs)

THMs (also called haloforms) are organic compounds based on the substitution of three of methane's four hydrogen atoms by halogen atoms. They arise in swimming pool water by reaction between the disinfectant and compounds either in the source water (usually humic acid) or introduced by bathers. Chlorine-based disinfectants will produce mainly trichloromethane (chloroform); bromine-based products mainly tribromomethane (bromoform). Dichloro-bromomethane and dibromochloromethane are also found. They may also be in the mains water supply to the pool, particularly when the source is surface water. THMs can be found in

The scale model pool at Cranfield University - used for measuring disinfection byproducts

pool water and in the air above the water. So swimmers can be exposed by absorption through the skin, by swallowing and by inhalation.

Chloroform is the commonest THM in freshwater pools - on average 86% by weight of total THMs. Although chloroform is the THM whose toxicity is best understood (it is a potential carcinogen), all THMs are considered undesirable.

The brominated THMs are both carcinogenic and mutagenic (causing birth defects). The official German standard (DIN) for swimming pool water does not include bromine-based disinfectants. FINA (Federation Internationale de Natation Amateur, the world governing body for competitive swimming) makes reference only to chlorine.

The UK standard for the sum of the concentrations of the four THMs in drinking water is 100 microgram (μg)/l as a three-monthly average. WHO recommends drinking water guideline values of:

- trichloromethane 200μg/l
- dichlorobromomethane 60μg/l
- dibromochloromethane 100μg/l
- tribromomethane 100μg/l.

The sum of the ratio of each concentration to its guideline value should not exceed 1. The new Drinking Water Directive contains a standard for the four THMs of 150 micrograms/l as a maximum.

It is not easy to translate standards from drinking water to pool water. But for competitive swimming there is a FINA-recommended maximum for THMs of 20μg/l.

UK mains water derived from surface waters often has a THM concentration of 20-100μg/l, and occasionally over 100μg/l. Although THM testing of pool water has been very patchy, it is clear that THM levels can be well over the drinking water guideline values above. Bromine-based disinfectants, for example, can produce levels of bromoform alone that are higher than 100μg/l. In most circumstances a well-run pool should be able to operate with total THM concentrations in the pool water below the drinking water standard of 100μg/l. When the THM concentration approaches or exceeds 100μg/l in the source water, every effort should be made to ensure that the THM concentration in the pool does not rise

significantly above that in the source water. This may mean considering water treatment with ozone.

THM monitoring is not recommended as a routine, as it is costly and difficult; but managers should be aware of the issue. It certainly makes sense to minimise THM levels, by good pre-swim hygiene, not over-loading the pool and minimising disinfectant use. Humic acid compounds in source water can be reduced through coagulation. PWTAG research at the Pool Water Research Foundation at Cranfield University has confirmed that adding large amounts of chemicals over a short period (eg shock dosing - superchlorination) increases THM generation. So does sudden increases in bathing load. This underlines the importance of keeping these two factors as steady as possible - by automatic monitoring and dosing and by close control of bathing load. Water treatment with ozone has traditionally been considered as a means of reducing THMs.

Dosing disinfectants before the filter, as recommended in this book, can also produce THMs. (The disinfectant reacts with pollutants on the filter.) But the benefits - reducing bacterial colonisation of the filter, segregating acid and disinfectant - outweigh that disadvantage (see page 52). In any case, the minimum use of chemicals advocated in this book (as well as minimising bather pollution through pre-swim showering) should reduce the impact on THM production.

But it is clear that THM will be generated, and released into the air, in any pool. So a critical factor in healthy swimming is to clear them away by good ventilation. This is dealt with in Chapter 19.

Chlorite and chlorate

Chlorite and chlorate sometimes appear in pool water when hypochlorite disinfectant is used (and with chlorine dioxide, which is a rarely used disinfectant in UK pools). There are no UK drinking water standards for chlorite or chlorate. WHO has not recommended a guideline value for chlorate because there are not enough toxicity data. Chlorite is a potential cause of methaemoglobinaemia, in which the blood loses some of its ability to carry oxygen. WHO recommends a provisional drinking water guideline value for chlorite of 200μg/l (provisional because difficulties in meeting a guideline value must never compromise disinfection). There is a UK guideline of 500µg/l for the total of chlorine dioxide and chlorite.

Bromate

Bromate is formed in pool water when ozone reacts with naturally occurring bromide in mains water (or with bromine-based disinfectant), particularly at high pH values. It may also be introduced during the electrolytic generation of hypochlorite. Bromate is a carcinogen. There is no UK standard for bromate in drinking water. WHO recommends a provisional guideline value of 25µg/l (provisional because of limitations in the analytical method for determining bromate). However, WHO is likely to move towards a toxicity-based guideline value of 3µg/l as analytical methods improve. The new Drinking Water Directive is likely to set a standard for bromate of 10µ/l.

Such guidelines reinforce the need to reduce chemical additions to the minimum required to maintain adequate disinfection. It may become necessary to measure bromate levels in pool water, to assess the extent of this problem.

Chapter 15

Microbiological monitoring

Microbiological problems should be insignificant in a well managed pool with an adequate disinfectant residual, a pH value maintained at the recommended level and regular filter backwashing. Nevertheless, samples of pool water should be tested at appropriate intervals to ensure that all is well. In general, a routine monthly test will suffice; but samples should also be taken before a pool is used for the first time, before it is put back into use after it has been shut down for repairs or cleaning, and if there are difficulties with the treatment system. Samples should also be tested when there is contamination, and as part of any investigation into possible adverse effects on bathers' health. If health effects are suspected, the consultant in communicable disease control, environmental health officer and director of the testing laboratory should be informed.

Nevertheless, certain infections have been associated with the use of swimming pools (see Chapter 14). These have almost invariably resulted from poor management or design faults, leading to contamination of the pool water with pathogenic (disease-producing) microorganisms. These bugs may come from bathers' faeces, blood, mucus, skin etc; or - in exceptional circumstances - from defects in an adjacent sewerage system.

They may also be of environmental origin. All natural water contains a variety of microorganisms with different optimum temperatures for growth; even mains drinking water may contain a few. Most of those capable of living in water will grow best at a temperature of around 22°C. Those normally associated with the human body will grow best at body temperature (37°C); most human pathogens will also grow best at this temperature.

In order to ensure their safety, people doing microbiological monitoring should be properly trained and work to a written protocol supported by a COSHH assessment.

COLONY (PLATE) COUNTS

The first microbiological test is the total viable (or colony) count, sometimes called the plate count. This indicates the number of bacteria present without differentiating in detail between the different kinds. It does not represent the total number of bacteria present in the water - only those capable of forming visible colonies in certain laboratory media under specified cultural conditions. In this test a volume of the water is mixed with a nutrient agar medium and incubated for a set time at a set temperature. Bacterial colonies become visible for assessment.

Varying the incubation temperature will favour the growth of different groups of bacteria. So incubation at 37°C gives an indication of the number of bacteria derived from bathers, possibly including any pathogens; incubation at 22°C will tend to inhibit the growth of these bacteria, but gives a better picture of the environmental organisms present in the pool - some of which may have come from the water supply.

As it gives more meaningful information about pathogenic bacteria, 37°C is the preferred temperature. Incubation for 24 hours is usually enough for the more significant bacteria to form colonies; little further information will be gained by extending it. Incubating a second culture at 22°C will give a more complete picture of the bacteria present in the water, but it will not greatly assist the assessment of the hygienic conditions in the pool.

Colony counts are usually expressed as colony forming units (cfu) per ml of water. They do not necessarily give an indication of microbiological safety, but give valuable information on the general quality of the pool water and whether the filtration and disinfection systems are operating satisfactorily.

TESTS FOR COLIFORM ORGANISMS

Coliform bacteria, particularly *Escherichia coli* (*E coli*), are normal inhabitants of the intestinal tract of man and warm-blooded animals, where they are present in great numbers. As they do not multiply in water, their presence in a water sample indicates faecal contamination and implies that pathogenic organisms from the bowel might also be present. Coliforms are the only organisms for which routine tests are universally recommended; coliform tests give further information on water quality, as an addition to colony counts.

In the laboratory, the presence of coliform organisms and their likely numbers in a sample of water may be readily determined, either by membrane filtration or the multiple-tube method. It must be appreciated, however, that both counts are subject to statistical variation within the methods themselves. And there is likely to be a further error introduced because the sample taken represents only a small proportion of the volume of water in the pool. In both methods, the results are expressed as the number of coliforms (and *E coli*) per 100ml.

For the membrane filtration method a measured volume of water is passed through a sterile membrane filter which retains the bacteria at its surface. The membrane is then placed on a selective culture medium which, during incubation, allows the coliforms to grow and form characteristic colonies. The number of colonies produced will provide a direct count of the number of coliforms and *E coli* in the volume of water examined. For the multiple tube method different volumes taken from the sample are added to a series of tubes containing a selective nutrient medium. The tubes are incubated for up to 48 hours and from the number showing evidence of growth, the most probable number (mpn) of coliforms and *E coli* in the original sample can be calculated.

PSEUDOMONAS AERUGINOSA

There is no general agreement as to the value of examining pool waters routinely for the presence of pseudomonads. However, they are widely distributed in the environment and may also be present in or on bathers. They are capable of growing in water even at relatively low temperatures and will readily colonise filters, particularly those containing activated carbon (see page 73). Most species of *Pseudomonas* are non-pathogenic for healthy people, but *Ps aeruginosa* can cause skin and ear infections, so its presence in pool water is undesirable. Its presence indicates colonisation of the filters (possibly other parts of the system) as a result of inadequate disinfectant levels and/or insufficient backwashing. However, it is unlikely to be present in large numbers when the colony count is within acceptable limits.

So testing for *Ps aeruginosa* may be considered to be an optional part of the routine microbiological surveillance of swimming pools. But it should be done when there is evidence of operational problems such as failure of disinfection affecting filters, transfer channels or balance tanks, or a deterioration in the quality of the pool water; also if there are health problems.

If high levels are found - over 100 colony forming units per 100ml, say - there is no need to shut down the pool. Instead: check water clarity; check residuals and pH; resample; backwash thoroughly; wait one turnover; resample. If things are still not right, or there is any confusion, the problem should be discussed with the microbiological lab and the local consultant in communicable disease control (CCDC).

Spa pools and whirlpools have different operating conditions, and *Ps aeruginosa* skin infections have been reported when the pool design or management is poor; so routine testing is recommended for these pools.

STAPHYLOCOCCUS AUREUS

Testing pool water routinely for staphylococci, particularly *Staph aureus*, has been proposed as a suitable indicator of poor microbiological quality. But staphylococci are almost invariably found when bathers are present. So testing for staphylococci is therefore recommended only as part of a wider investigation into the quality of the water when health problems associated with the pool are suspected.

OTHER MICROORGANISMS

If there has been contamination, or if health effects have been associated with use of the pool, it may be advisable to examine additional water samples for suspected pathogens. These might include *Cryptosporidium*, *Giardia* and viruses (and *Legionella pneumophila* in spas). Advice should first be sought from the local public health authorities and an expert microbiologist, usually from the Public Health Laboratory Service.

ASSESSING MICROBIOLOGICAL QUALITY

Taken together, the colony count and the test for coliforms provide the simplest means of assessing the microbiological quality of swimming pool water.

- If the colony count is not more than 10cfu per ml at 37°C for 24 hours, and there are no coliforms or *E coli* present, it can be assumed that the hygienic conditions and operational management of the pool were satisfactory at the time the sample was taken.
- Occasionally a colony count of between 10 and 100cfu/ml will be found. This is acceptable provided no coliforms (or *E coli*) are present and the operating conditions of the pool are satisfactory.
- However, a consistently raised colony count of 10-100cfu/ml may require investigation.
- Colony counts in excess of 100cfu per ml clearly indicate that operating conditions are unsatisfactory and require investigation.
- If coliform organisms are also present, there is likely to be a serious defect in the pool operating system such as a failure of the disinfection process and/or a problem with the chemical balance of the pool (including the pH value), or the filtration system, which will require immediate attention.
- Occasionally a few (less than 10) coliforms may be found in the absence of *E coli* and with an unremarkable colony count. This may be acceptable provided the residual disinfectant concentration and pH value are satisfactory and coliforms are not found in consecutive samples.

With chlorinated isocyanurates and BCDMH, elevated colony counts are relatively common and often stable. But if there is a significant change in the counts, action should be taken.

Sampling procedure

Misleading information on pool water quality will result from incorrect sampling procedures. Sample containers must be constructed of a material that will not affect the quality of the sample either microbiologically or chemically. Although a good quality glass container will meet these requirements, the risk of breakage in the pool environment has favoured the use of shatterproof plastic-coated glass containers. All-plastic containers can be used provided they do not react with microorganisms or chemicals in the water; not all are suitable. The required capacity is usually 200-500ml.

For microbiological examination, the bottle must be sterile and contain an agent that neutralises the disinfectant used in the pool water. Sodium thiosulphate (18mg/l) is the agent for chlorine and bromine-based disinfectants. Clearly the testing laboratory must be advised before sampling if any other disinfectant is used. Sodium thioglycollate (10%m/V) is suitable for pools using copper/silver ions for disinfection (with thiosulphate as well if, as is likely, a chlorine residual is also used). For polymeric biguanides, lecithin (3%m/V) with Tween 80 (20%m/V) is used.

To take the microbiological sample, the stopper or cap is first removed with one hand, making sure that nothing touches the inside of the bottle or cap. The bottle is then immersed to about 150mm below the surface when the bottle is tilted to face horizontally towards the direction of flow and allowed to fill. On removal from the water, the cap is immediately replaced and the sample sent to the laboratory without delay.

The active disinfectant residual and pH value should be determined in a separate sample from the same site when the microbiological sample is taken, and this information should accompany the first sample to the laboratory. The second sample must be taken separately into a container without a neutralising agent. If this cannot be done at the poolside, or if the concentration of dimethylhydantoin or other chemical is required, a separate sample must be taken into a suitable container.

The most appropriate site for taking a single sample is where the water velocity is low, away from any inlets. Depending on the size of the pool, it may be advisable to take samples from other sites. Many leisure pools will have additional features such as flumes, islands and backwaters with a complex system of water flow - so several samples should be taken to get an overall picture of the water quality.

Sampling frequency

It should not be necessary to take frequent samples for microbiological examination, provided the correct residual disinfectant concentration and pH value, as measured directly at the pool, are maintained. (See Chapter 13.) For most pools, a sample taken once a month as a random check should provide adequate assurance of quality. This should be done when the pool is heavily loaded. More frequent samples should be taken when there is any reason to suppose that there has been a deterioration in quality. More frequent sampling may be needed for pools that are persistently heavily used, for teaching and hydrotherapy pools, or new pools being commissioned.

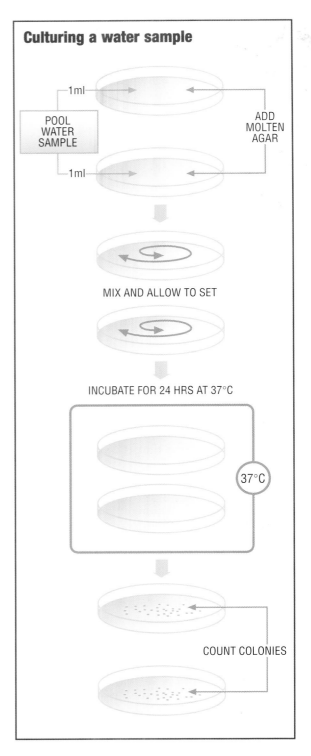

Culturing a water sample

POOL WATER SAMPLE
1ml
1ml
ADD MOLTEN AGAR

MIX AND ALLOW TO SET

INCUBATE FOR 24 HRS AT 37°C

37°C

COUNT COLONIES

Microbiological methods

Appropriate methods for testing water samples for colony counts, coliforms (including *E coli*), *Ps aeruginosa* and staphylococci are detailed in *Report 71 - The Microbiology of Water 1994: Part 1 - Drinking Water*. See Bibliography.

Guidelines for routine samples (taken approximately monthly) are given as follows.

Colony count (37°C for 24 hours)
Not more than 10cfu/ml

Total coliforms
Absent in l00ml
Less than l0 per l00ml is acceptable provided it does not happen in consecutive samples, there are no *Escherichia coli*, the colony count is less than 10cfu/ml and the residual disinfectant concentration and pH values are within the recommended ranges

Escherichia coli
Absent in l00ml

Pseudomonas aeruginosa
Absent in 100ml for all spas and whirlpools
(and as optional additional quality assurance in conventional pools

Chapter 16

Pool water chemicals

A swimming pool building - especially if it also a leisure centre - will inevitably contain a lot of different chemicals. Many will be to do with pool water treatment - disinfectants, water balancing chemicals, coagulants, algicides. Others will be the sort of cleaners, etc found in any public building - often in large quantities and of a great variety (see Chapter 22). Making sure the right chemicals are chosen, and that they are used safely and effectively, is one of the first priorities of pool managers - as detailed in Chapter 20.

This chapter contains the information necessary for that responsibility to be discharged - including the first comprehensive listing of those chemicals officially approved on safety grounds. There is a section on algicides.

SAFETY APPROVAL

There is an important source of information on pool water treatment chemicals. It is produced by the Department of the Environment, Transport and the Regions (DETR) Committee on Chemicals and Materials of Construction for use in Public Water Supply and Swimming Pools. (Contacts etc are on page 137.) At intervals, the Committee produces a roughly eight-page List of products 'approved' as 'unobjectionable on health grounds for the treatment of swimming pools'. This is published in the Institute of Sport and Recreation Management magazine, *Recreation*. There are over 160 products listed - many of them generic chemical names (eg sodium hypochlorite), but also many brand names, including some water treatment equipment.

The wording that introduces the List is crucial (and sometimes misunderstood or used to mislead). Approval is based on detailed chemical and toxicological data, but is on public health grounds only. It is not a recommendation; in particular it carries no

endorsement of the efficacy or effectiveness of the product. So promotional statements like 'approved by the DETR' should be taken with a pinch of sodium chloride.

It is worth quoting further from the List.

' *The following products approved by the Committee on Chemicals and Materials of Construction for use in Public Water Supply and Swimming Pools are considered to be unobjectionable on health grounds for the treatment of swimming pool water provided that they are used in accordance with the manufacturers' instructions and recommended doses (as notified to the Committee) and any conditions referred to in the approval. When approving chemicals for use in the treatment of swimming pool water, the Committee considers whether the use of the product under the conditions notified by the applicant represents a risk to the health of bathers.*

Approval by the Committee may not be taken as a favourable assessment of the performance or fitness for purpose of any product. The Committee is aware that some bathers may experience skin irritation and rashes following exposure to some swimming pool waters. It is recommended that pool operators follow [Swimming Pool Water] produced by the Pool Water Treatment Advisory Group, to ensure good pool management to minimise such incidents. The Committee also recommends that all such bather complaints are investigated.'

Although the Committee's approvals are voluntary and have no statutory basis, PWTAG is happy to return the Committee's compliment and firmly recommend that pool operators use only water treatment chemicals approved by the Committee. These chemicals are detailed on pages 104-108 - with extra information on hazards and incompatibility to that given in the Committee's List.

PURITY AND STRENGTH

It is often difficult to determine the purity and strength of chemicals from manufacturers' or suppliers' literature. It is important, though, that the percentage active ingredient is known when comparing products. But differences may relate to different characteristics. For example, a particular tablet may be designed to dissolve more quickly than one with a higher percentage of the same active ingredient.

Product specifications should be requested, and where necessary certificates of analysis or certificates confirming conformity to specification.

Purity is to some degree assured for List chemicals, as their degree of impurity is part of the information requested by the Committee, and is taken into consideration before a public health approval is granted. If more information on purity is needed, the manufacturers must be approached.

MATERIAL SAFETY DATA SHEETS

MSDSs must be available from suppliers and manufacturers of preparations and chemicals that are dangerous for supply. This responsibility is set out in regulation 6 of the Chemical (Hazard, Information and Packaging for Supply) Regulations 1994 (CHIP2). MSDSs should provide information on the hazard (ie the inherent properties) and should be used in the risk assessment (see below).

MSDSs must be provided free by suppliers by the time the product is delivered. Updates are also free, as are MSDSs for anyone using chemicals at work. A typical MSDS is reproduced on page 129. All must have information (from the supplier) under 16 headings:

1 identification of the substance and manufacturer/supplier
2 composition/information on ingredients
3 hazards identification
4 first-aid measures
5 fire-fighting measures
6 accidental release measures
7 handling and storage
8 exposure controls/personal protection
9 physical and chemical properties
10 stability and reactivity
11 toxicological information
12 ecological information
13 disposal considerations
14 transport information
15 regulatory information
16 other information.

Installers, too, have a responsibility to provide relevant information on plant safety, etc - which may include MSDSs. There must be MSDSs for test kit reagent chemicals as well. MSDSs form one basis for making a formal risk assessment.

RISK ASSESSMENT

The Management of Health and Safety at Work Regulations 1992 require all employers and the self-employed to do a risk assessment of their work activities. For pool chemicals, this assessment should be done in terms of the Control of Substances Hazardous to Health Regulations 1994 (COSHH).

The first step is for the employer (the pool manager) to assess the risk of each chemical. This must be done by a competent person - a member of the management team for a small, stand-alone pool; often a specialist team in a multi-function local authority department. (There is more on management in the next chapter.) This process will need to call on the experience and knowledge of others. For example, the assessor will need to know about:
- other chemicals on site - by reference to MSDSs, etc
- storage and handling arrangements
- site location in relation to the impact of a chemical accident
- staff training and competence in using chemicals.

Where this asssessment is done under COSHH, there is no need for further assessment to comply with the Management of Health and Safety at Work Regulations 1992 - provided the initial assessment is regularly reviewed and remains valid.

Risk elimination
The next step under COSHH is to prevent or control exposure to hazardous substances. This should include consideration of swimmers, spectators, other users and staff. Prevention is obviously best: the manager should consider whether this can be achieved by substituting a less harmful substance, or

one that is more compatible with other chemicals on site. This may reduce the risk of fire, explosion or the production of toxic gases.

Only where prevention is not reasonably practicable can the manager turn to adequate control as a legitimate second option. And this must be by measures other than personal protection equipment. Instead, the risk must be reduced to acceptable limits by control measures which should be systematically recorded, as recommended by the Health & Safety Executive:

- identification of the hazards
- identification of who might be harmed and how
- evaluation of the risks arising from the hazards, and decisions about precautions
- recording the findings
- regular review of the assessments and any necessary revisions.

An obvious way to reduce risk is to limit the range of chemicals used. Clearly managers are more liable to censure for not eliminating risk if they use two incompatible chemicals where one would have done. In any case, the combination of chemicals used must be considered, and its effect on the composition of the water and the air.

The management of this is dealt with in Chapter 20.

THE CHEMICALS

The tables on the next five pages list all the chemicals approved (on safety grounds only) by the DETR Committee on Chemicals and Materials of Construction for use in Public Water Supply and Swimming Pools in July 1998. They are grouped by type of chemical, with information on use, form, hazard and trade names.

Basic chemicals - sodium hypochlorite, sodium carbonate, etc - are also approved without brand names. It is important, if buying these, to make sure they are suitable for swimming pools - not agricultural grade, for example.

Algicides

Outdoor pools and some indoor pools exposed to sunlight may experience problems with algal growth, particularly where the pool hydraulics are poor. Foreign objects, like canoes, can introduce algae. Even the phosphates sometimes put in mains water can encourage algal growth; they should be flocculated out as part of the water treatment regime.

Chlorine is an effective algicide, but it will not compensate for the effect of poor hydraulics. Chlorinated isocyanurates help. Growth can develop very quickly given warmth and sunlight; the longer it persists, the more difficult it is to remove. So it is important to act immediately there are signs of algal growth. With no-one in the pool, brush and vacuum off algae, increase disinfectant levels and filter off the detached algae.

If this is unsuccessful, it will be necessary to use a proprietary algicide. Only algicides which have been approved as being unobjectionable on health grounds by the DETR Committee on Chemicals and Materials (see page 101) should be used. Most of the approved products are based on quaternary ammonium and polyoxyiminio compounds; or copper-based.

But the main treatment is getting the pool management right from the start. Algal growth should not happen if the pool is designed and operated correctly.

CHEMICAL	TRADE NAME	USE	FORM	HAZARD	INCOMPATIBILITY
Sodium hypochlorite	Bridos Chlorine Liquid Briswim Hispec Stabilised Chlorine Liquid Bridos SP Grade Hypochlorite Feedchlor	Disinfectant	Liquid Liquid Liquid Liquid	Toxic to aquatic organisms. Very toxic to fish. Causes burn to skin, eyes and respiratory system. Inhalation of vapour fumes can cause severe breathing difficulty	Contact with acids liberates toxic gas (chlorine). Avoid acids, ammonia and ammonium salts, methanol, hydrocarbons copper, nickel, iron, monel metal. Dangerous reactions with organic materials
Calcium hypochlorite	Chloryte HTH Regular, HTH Duration Tablets, Pulsar Plus Calcium Hypochlorite Briquettes, Pulsar Plus Calcium Hypochlorite Tablets, HTH Dry Chlorinator Briquettes, HTH Dry Chlorinator Tablets, HTH Easi-flo Briquettes, HTH Easi-flo Tablets. HTH Easi-flo Briswim Supershock Chlorine Granules Pittchlor Klorman Sanitabs CTX-120/121 Hypochlorite Granules/Tablets	Disinfectant	Granules Granules, tablets, briquettes Tablet or granules Granules Tablets Tablets or granules	Oxidising and corrosive Oxidiser, eye and skin hazard; corrosive; lung toxin. Do not inhale. Highly toxic to aquatic flora and fauna	Extensive including household and pool products. Calcium hypochlorite should not be mixed with anything but water. Explosive reactions with organics - oils, greases, etc. Avoid acids, nitrogen containing compounds, dry powder fire extinguishers (containing mono-ammonium phosphates), corrosive, flammable or combustible materials
Trichloroisocyanuric acid	Astral Trichlor Tablets, Granules, Powder Flexitab Chlorine Tablets Brichlor Chlorine Tablets Chlorilong 250, Chloriklar Bayrobloc 600 Biocide 50, SD50, SD200 ACL90 Tablets, ACL90 plus Fi-Clor Tablets Mini Fi-Clor Tablets Maxi Fi-Clor Tri Tabs Fi-Gard 90, Fi-Buoy	Disinfectant	Tablets. granules powder	Oxidiser, skin corrosive, eye hazard, oral toxin, lung toxin	Organic materials, oils, grease, sawdust, reducing agents, nitrogen containing materials, other oxidisers, acids, bases, dry fire extinguishers containing ammonium compounds
Sodium dichloroisocyanurate	Astral Dichlor Granules Chlorifix X100, Chlorifix 60 Biocide 550 ACL 60	Disinfectant	Granules	Corrosive. Causes eye and skin damage. Irritating to nose and throat. Harmful or fatal if swallowed. Will burn with the evolution of chlorine and equally toxic gases. Strong oxidising agent	Keep concentrated material dry. Avoid contact with easily oxidisable organic material; ammonia, urea, or similar nitrogen containing compounds; inorganic reducing compounds; floor sweeping compounds; calcium hypochlorite, alkalis
Sodium dichloroisocyanurate dihydrate	Brichlor PlusChlorine Granules, Briswim Fast Dissolving Chlorine Tablets ACL 56 Fi-Clor Granules	Disinfectant	Granules, tablets	Corrosive. Causes eye and skin damage. Irritating to nose and throat. Harmful or fatal if swallowed. Will burn with the evolution of chlorine and equally toxic gases. Strong oxidising agent	Keep concentrated material dry. Avoid contact with easily oxidisable organic material; ammonia, urea, or similar nitrogen containing compounds; inorganic reducing compounds; floor sweeping compounds; calcium hypochlorite, alkalis

Active ingredient	Product name	Function	Granules or powder	Skin and eye irritant	Oxidisers
Cyanuric acid	Briswim Chlorine Stabiliser, Fi-Clor Chlorine Stabiliser	Stabiliser		Solid undiluted product is irritating to the skin and eyes	Avoid contact with strong acids and bases, low molecular weight organic materials, readily oxidisable materials and strong reducing agents
Bromochloro-dimethylhydantoin	Aquabrome	Disinfectant	Tablets		Strong acids, bases, Oxidising materials
BCDMH/DCDMH/DCEMH	Bromisan	Disinfectant	Briquettes	Contact with combustible material may cause fire. Harmful if swallowed. Causes burns. May cause sensitisation by skin contact	
Polymeric biguanide hydrochloride	Baquacil	Disinfectant	Liquid	Irritating to skin. May cause sensitisation by skin contact. Vapour or aerosol, if generated, can cause irritation of the eyes, nose and respiratory tract. Very toxic to fish. Very toxic to aquatic organisms	Not compatible with chlorinating chemicals or bromine/iodine donors. Not compatible with ionic sterilisers, copper based QAC algicides, anionic detergents, water softening chemicals. persulphate oxidants or ozone generating devices
Tetrachlorodecaoxide	HydroXan	Oxidant	Liquid	Ingestion of undiluted material may cause oxidising effect. Undiluted material may be irritating on inhalation	Strong acids
Sodium bromide	Poolcure	Disinfectant additive	Liquid	Concentrated product is skin and eye irritant	
Calcium chloride	Briswim Water Hardener Flakes, Poolcal	Raise calcium hardness	Flakes / Powder	Irritating to eyes, prolonged contact may cause skin irritation	Strong acids
Sodium bisulphate	Pool minus/pH Minus, Astral pH Minus, Briswim Dry Acid Granules	Lower pH and total alkalinity	Powder, Solid, Granules	Dust is highly irritating to skin, especially when wet. Risk of serious damage to eyes	Strong oxidising agents. Metals, alkalis and chlorinated substances
Formulation	Pool Plus	Raise pH and alkalinity	Powder		Acids, ammonium hydrogen phosphate, sodium, potassium
Formulation	pH Plus	Raise pH	Powder		Acids, ammonium hydrogen phosphate, sodium, potassium
Formulation	Alkbuild	Raise pH and alkalinity	Liquid	Causes severe burns to skin, eyes and mucous membranes	Avoid all acids and metals
Formulation based on sodium hexametaphosphate	Corroban 64	Precipitates Ca and Mg hardness	Liquid	Harmful if swallowed or absorbed through the skin	
Magnesium oxide	Lycal 93/12, 93/34, 93/711	Raise pH	Powder	Nuisance dust	
Sulphuric acid	Bayrol pH Minus	Lower pH	Liquid	Corrosive causes severe burns	Avoid organic materials and metals

CHEMICAL	TRADE NAME	USE	FORM	HAZARD	INCOMPATIBILITY
Sodium hydroxide	Bayrol pH Plus	Raise pH	Liquid	Corrosive, has a strong corrosive action	Can react violently with acids and many organic chemicals particularly chlorinated hydrocarbons. Aluminium, zinc, brass and tin are attacked with the evolution of hydrogen
Sodium carbonate	Astral pH Plus Briswim Alkali Granules	Raise pH	Granules Granules	Do not ingest. The repeated and extended exposure may produce ulceration and damage to the cornea. Irritating to eyes, respiratory tract and skin	Acids, quicklimes, aluminium and zinc
Sodium thiosulphate	Briswim Chlorine Neutraliser Granules	Chlorine neutraliser	Crystals		
Sodium bicarbonate	Briswim pH Stabiliser Granules	Raise total alkalinity	Granules		Acids. Do not add to pool water at same time as other pool products
Sodium polyphosphate	Briswim Iron/Calcium Sequestrant	Iron/calcium sequestrant	Powder		
Modified potassium polyacrylate	SASE	Dispersant and scale inhibitor	Liquid	Irritating to eyes and skin	Strong acids
Magnesium hydroxide	Magnaspheres Fi-Gard pH Neutraliser Hydromag G Hydromag CM	Raise pH pH neutraliser raise pH raise pH	Powder Agglomerate Granules Dolomite	Nuisance dust Irritating to eyes	Strong acids
Hydrogen peroxide	Baqua Shock	Clarifier	Liquid	Causes burns. Harmful by inhalation and if swallowed	
Formulation	Waterguard S	Corrosion inhibitor	Liquid	May cause caustic burns to skin and eyes, the danger greater with hot liquid. Harmful by ingestion causing internal irritation	Acids, fluorine, wood, aluminium zinc and their alloys
Formulation	Waterguard P	Corrosion inhibitor	Liquid		
Activated carbon	Eurocarb HRO/YAO/PHO Steam Activated Carbon	Filter medium	Granules, extrudates or powder		
Silicon dioxide	Zeoclere 30	Filter medium	Granules		

Active substance	Product name	Function	Form	Hazard/Precautions
Aluminium sulphate	Briswim Granular Floc	Filter aid (flocculant)	Granules	Avoid contact with strong alkalis, chlorites, hypochlorites, sulphites, cyanide, sulphides and most metal surfaces
	Astral Flocculant in Cartridges	Filter acid (flocculant)	Solid	Dust highly irritating to skin, especially when wet and risk of serious damage to eyes
	Briswim Goldifloc Fine Filter Tablets	Filter acid (flocculant)	Tablet	Irritant to the eyes
	Superflock C	Flocculating/clarifying	Tablets	
Aluminium oxide silicate	HydroSan	Coagulant	Liquid	Skin and eye irritant
Polymeric quaternary ammonium compound	Bubond 65 / Hicat-1	Flocculating/clarifying	Liquid	Irritating to eyes / Do not use in concentrated form with aluminium, zinc, or galvanised equipment
Quaternary ammonium polymer	Fi-Chem Cleanse	Flocculating/clarifying	Liquid	Toxic to fish. As a general precaution avoid prolonged contact with the product
Blend of polymeric quaternary ammonium and aluminium based coagulants/flocculants	Fi-Chem Flocculant	Flocculating/clarifying	Liquid	As a general precaution avoid prolonged contact with the product
Aqueous solution of polyaluminiumchloride	Dinofloc Aktiv Flocculant	Flocculating/clarifying	Liquid	
Polyoxyethylene (dimethyliminio) ethylene (dimethyliminio) ethylene dichloride	WSCP/Busan 77	Algicide/biocide	Liquid	Avoid contact with anionic products
Polyhydroxyethylene (dimethyliminio) ethylene-(dimethyliminio) methylene dichloride	WSCP-2/Busan 79	Algicide/biocide	Liquid	Avoid contact with anionic products
Poly 2-hydroxyethylene (dimethyliminio)-2-hydroxpropylene (dim ethyliminio) methylene dichloride	APCA	Algicide/biocide	Liquid	Concentrated product is toxic to fish
Copper citrate complex	Kleenpool Algicide	Algicide/biocide	Liquid	Toxic to fish and aquatic life

CHEMICAL	TRADE NAME	USE	FORM	HAZARD	INCOMPATIBILITY
Polyquaternary ammonium chloride	Microtreat 2040 Kintrol 580 Albricide WS Glokill PQ Goldifloc Cationic Liquid Bayroplus Poolcide Biocide BQ	Algicide/biocide Algicide/biocide Algicide/biocide Algicide/biocide Algicide/biocide Algicide/biocide Algicide/biocide	Liquid Liquid Liquid Liquid Liquid Liquid Liquid	Harmful if swallowed. Irritating to skin and eyes. Toxic to fish.	Strong oxidising agents
Alkyl dimethyl benzyl ammonium chloride	Rhodaquat RP 50 Briswim Algicide Liquid Britoc Algicide Liquid	Algicide/biocide Algicide/biocide Algicide/biocide	Liquid Liquid Liquid	Toxic to aquatic organisms	Strong oxidising agents
Hydrogen peroxide	Bayrosoft	Algicide/biocide	Liquid	Corrosive to skin, eyes and mucous membranes. Not combustible but will contribute to the combustion of other materials	Acids, alkalis, metals, salts of metals, reducing agents, organic materials, flammable substances
Potassium peroxymonosulphate/ potassium bisulphate & polyquaternary compound	Bayroklar Duo Tab Bayroklar Spa & Bayroplus Spa	Algicide/biocide	Tablet	Harmful if swallowed, causes burns, contact with combustible materials may cause fire. Danger of decomposition when exposed to heat, with evolution of sulphur dioxide	Acids, alkalis, metals, salts of metals, reducing agents, organic materials, flammable substances
Polyquaternary ammonium chloride & polycarbonic acid	Puripool Super	Algicide/biocide	Liquid		
Alkylbenzyl dimethyl ammonium chloride	Kintrol 524	Algicide/biocide	Liquid	Harmful if swallowed, corrosive to the skin and mucous membranes	Strong oxidising agents

Chapter 17

Delivery of chemicals

Most of the factors determining successful delivery arrangements should have been settled during the design process (Chapter 3). Such planning must taken into account the types of disinfectant and other chemicals being used (Chapter 16).

Disinfectants are delivered as liquids, gases or solids:

- sodium hypochlorite - liquid in plastic 5, 25 & 45l containers; and in 1,000l intermediate bulk containers (IBCs) for transfer into the plant room's bulk storage tank
- calcium hypochlorite - in drums (granules 40kg, tablets 45kg); plastic or metal with plastic liners (smaller, more expensive packs are available)
- chlorine gas - 33, 55 & 71kg cylinders of liquid chlorine under pressure
- sodium dichloroisocyanurate granules - normally 5, 10 & 25kg plastic pails
- trichloroisocyanuric acid sticks or tablets - normally 2-25kg plastic containers
- bromochlorodimethylhydantoin tablets - normally 5kg plastic pails

Chlorine gas suppliers, in particular, will deliver only to safe sites - which applies to delivery as well as plant room design and management.

Ancillary chemicals come as:

- hydrochloric acid - 5, 25 & 45l plastic containers; and in 1,000l IBCs
- carbon dioxide - in 22.6kg cylinders, and mini-bulk vacuum insulated vessels of 180 or 270kg
- sodium bisulphate granules (dry acid) - 25kg plastic sacks & pails, 7kg plastic cans
- sodium carbonate granules (soda ash) - 25kg plastic sacks & pails, 5kg plastic cans
- sodium bicarbonate powder - 25kg paper sacks & plastic pails, 5kg plastic cans
- calcium chloride flake - 25kg bags & plastic pails, 5kg plastic jerricans

- aluminium sulphate - 25kg plastic pails & sacks & 50kg sacks (kibbled); 25kg sacks & pails (granules)
- liquid polyaluminium chloride (PAC) - 25l cans
- polyaluminium sulpho-silicate (PASS) - 20l packs

Acids should be delivered in IBCs only if the 1,000l will last six weeks or less.

Cylinders and drums - like all chemical containers - should be clearly labelled for content. Packaging and labelling should comply with the Chemicals (Hazard, Information and Packaging for Supply) Regulations 1994, and the Carriage of Dangerous Goods by Road and Rail (Classification, Packaging and Labelling) Regulations 1994. Chlorine transport emergency cards (TREMCARDS) are required for certain products.

Precaution cards and first aid instructions should be displayed for each product, close to the offloading areas. See Chapter 18.

ACCESS

Clearly, the nearer delivery vehicles can get to the chemical store the better. (See below for bulk delivery.) The access road and the off-loading area should allow a clear, safe approach with minimal manoeuvring. Unloading should not be on the public highway; if it has to be - for some good reason - the local authority must give permission, and warning signs and pedestrian barriers must be used.

The offloading area should be concrete or equivalent, at the same level as the store, with a drain to a sump (or a local authority-approved drain) and a good supply of hosed running water. Written procedures to deal with spillages must be approved, understood and available to staff. (Spilt, dry materials can sometimes be swept up, stored and used at an early opportunity.) The disposal of contaminated waste is subject to waste disposal regulations.

The offloading area should be clearly labelled with the appropriate warning signs. Incompatible materials (eg acid and alkali) delivered in the same vehicle should be effectively segregated on the vehicle, and throughout their delivery into separate storage.

OFFLOADING

In general, cylinders and other containers of over 25kg will be delivered either on vehicles with a tail lift, or on platform vehicles with a slide or skid that allows containers to be lowered to the ground. A delivery dock at the same height as the delivery vehicle is an acceptable alternative, as is a forklift truck. The driver may need help offloading (and no delivery should go ahead if there is no-one to receive it). The responsibility for offloading and onloading is joint between customer and driver. The driver's responsibility ends when the container reaches ground or dock level. No container must ever be dropped to the ground.

Lifting gear may also be used. The safe working load (SWL) should not be exceeded, and regular inspection, testing and certification is crucial.

Bulk delivery of sodium hypochlorite

The connection of IBCs to bulk storage tanks of sodium hypochlorite is a critical process, needing careful preparation physically and organisationally. The tank should, ideally, be on an outside wall in the storage room, so that its level indicator (the other side of the wall) can be read during delivery. If not, and the fill point is remote from the tank, a fillguard alarm system with warning lights (whose operation can be checked before each delivery) should be fitted. The chemical should not be pumped across a pavement. If there is a permanent fill line, it must not pass through public areas, and may need to be protected. It should drain back to the tank.

Bulk tanks are normally 1,500l, to take 1,000l from the IBC. The tank should be marked so that it is clear when it needs to be filled, and when it is full.

The pipework should be specific to the delivery of that product, to prevent delivery hoses being incorrectly connected up. It is important that any other chemical delivered in bulk has a separate, different size or type of connection. Pipework fill points should be clearly labelled and locked when not in use.

The whole process should be the specific responsibility of a nominated member of staff. That supervisor should have had suitable training on the product and its operation, and:

- have a clear knowledge of the offloading procedures and hypochlorite handling precautions
- supervise the offloading operation throughout
- make sure the right product is being delivered and that the quantity supplied corresponds to that ordered
- make sure that there is room in the tank for the full quantity being delivered
- pay particular attention to the level in the bulk tank, before and during offloading
- check that the drain valves on the storage tank filling line are closed
- instruct the driver to connect the flexible hose to the correct intake pipe; check that the connection has been made correctly, and that there is no restriction to flow
- sign the discharge consent notice before instructing the driver to start pumping; and stop the driver from pumping if the procedure goes wrong in any way, or when the correct amount has been offloaded
- when the right amount has been offloaded, close the valve on the filling line; when drainage stops, instruct the driver to disconnect the flexible hose
- deal with any spillages and drainage by washing them away to sump or drain
- sign the discharge consent and consignment notices after delivery.

A written delivery procedure should be agreed with the supplier (in accordance with COSHH data sheets), placed on the safety file, and regularly reviewed. The pool's written emergency plan should cover bulk storage as well as all chemicals stored on site. The appropriate protective clothing should be worn.

TRANSPORT FROM OFFLOADING AREA TO STORE

Chemical containers should not be left unattended at the offloading site, especially where it is open to the public. In any case, materials should be stored away in a cool place as soon as possible - especially sodium hypochlorite, whose decomposition is accelerated by sunlight (causing pressure rise and possible fracture of the container).

Containers should be kept upright, and never rolled. Nothing of 45 litres or over should be lifted by one person; or even two, ideally. Instead, custom-built wheeled carriers should always be used. Any carrier used for corrosive liquid containers should have a warning label. Some containers (of sodium hypochlorite, for example) have ventilated caps. Such containers should be handled carefully after transit, in case there is corrosive liquid on the outside.

If different chemicals are on the same carrier, they should be adequately segregated. Acid and alkali should not be transported together on the same carrier; nor should calcium hypochlorite and chloroisocyanurates.

The HSE book, *Managing Health and Safety in Swimming Pools* (see Bibliography, page 138) is a source of information on handling chemicals - which should be studied when designing systems for transferring pool chemicals from offloading to bunded storage areas. Protective clothing should always be worn in case of spillage or the need to handle a damaged container. In general, materials should not be transferred into any container not designed for that purpose. Empty containers should not be left on site, and never used as rubbish bins, etc. Eyewash stations should be available.

Cylinders

Cylinders of chlorine or carbon dioxide should be moved as soon as possible into the store, on purpose-built wheeled carriers with a clamp or chain that secures the cylinders in an upright position. The protective cap, dome or guard should always be in position over the valve during handling. Cylinders must be kept upright at all times, though they can be moved over short distances by rotating the whole cylinders, keeping them nearly upright. They should never be left unsecured, or causing an obstruction, or near a heat source.

If chlorine gas cylinders have to be moved from the main store to a distant point of use, an open vehicle must be used. Cylinders must be securely fixed in an upright position in the vehicle; a TREMCARD should be displayed; and the appropriate warning notices should be fixed to all doors.

Cylinders should not be dropped or treated roughly; they are heavy and should not, ideally, be lifted. Protective gloves and steel-capped boots should be worn.

Someone specifically trained for it should transport cylinders from the store to their point of use.

Chapter 18

Storage of chemicals

The principles underlying storage of pool chemicals are those that apply at all stages from delivery (Chapter 17) to disposal: chemicals must be treated with the respect their individual risks demand, and kept apart - both from each other and from the rest of the building. So a new design should avoid different chemicals being stored togther or in an open plant room - although this can be difficult on existing installations. The stores must be carefully planned and associated risks assessed. Access to the store should be limited to authorised personnel.

THE STORE

Storage room design needs to take into account primarily siting, construction materials and ventilation. Underlying each of these considerations must be the risks from fire and spillage.

Siting

Storage rooms should have an outside wall, on the same level as the delivery, ideally (for easier transport of chemicals, dealing with leaks, etc) and at least 10 metres away from public areas, thoroughfares, ventilation intakes, doors and windows. They should be vandal-resistant, accessible only to those authorised, and have warning signs on any doors and windows. They must be protected from frost, and the need to avoid excessive temperatures (depending on the chemical) means that the position of the store relative to boilers and calorifiers needs to be considered.

Where it is not possible for the store to be on an outside wall (perhaps in an existing installation) special attention must be paid to ventilation and access, bearing in mind the principles here.

Fire risk   The twin possibilities of fire in the store and fire elsewhere in the building make it essential that the store's walls be non-combustible and fire-resistant (1hour minimum). Nevertheless, a fire elsewhere in the building might increase the temperature in the store, causing containers to deform and even rupture. That means a risk of leakage, further fire, the release of dangerous fumes, and explosion. A storage room at ground level will facilitate the removal of containers in the event of such problems. No flammable materials should be stored in or close to the store.

Spillage   Spillage which might release chlorine or bromine is more of a problem with storage rooms below ground level; such siting is not recommended. If storage is below ground level, correct bunding (see opposite) is particularly crucial. (Chlorine gas - opposite - must never be stored below ground level.) Any underfloor ducting should be sealed to prevent leakage outside the store.

Corrosion   The atmosphere in the store is likely to be corrosive, so the room and any ventilation plant must be adequately corrosion resistant.

Ventilation

Ventilation is important (except in the sealed chlorine gas system described below) for the dispersal of fumes and to cope with the consequences of any accident. Stores must be ventilated to the outside air, by louvred doors, windows and low-level air vents. If through draft is not sufficient, a low-level exhaust fan, operated by a switch outside the store, should be installed. Four changes of air per hour (12 for chlorine gas) is necessary - and discharge, whether natural or mechanical, must be at least 10 metres (25m for chlorine gas) from public areas, doors, windows, ventilation intakes, etc. The prevailing wind directions should also be taken into account.

STORAGE OF CHLORINE GAS AND HYPOCHLORITES

The details of storage are dealt with here under the headings of the individual disinfectant chemicals. But there are some general principles that apply to these and other chemicals.

- All containers, and filling, feed and delivery lines, must be clearly labelled - including corrosive warnings as appropriate.
- Disinfectant and ancillary chemicals should not be stored in the same room/area as any other chemicals or materials - in particular, petrol, oils, solvents, fertilisers, other strong acids or alkalis, ammonia and its compounds, and cleaning materials.
- All containers should be kept securely closed, cool and dry. Chemicals supplied in paper or plastic sacks should be placed in plastic bins before opening, and securely closed after use.
- Non-returnable containers should be flushed out with plenty of water before disposal by the appropriate authority.
- Products no longer required should be safely disposed of.

Chlorine gas

The only part of a chlorine gas disinfection system at which the gas is under pressure is the cylinder - so strict control of storage is vital. Any potential user should consult with HSE as well as this chapter. One specific protection against leaks is a pneumatic auto cylinder shutdown, triggered by a signal from a fume detector.

Chlorine stores should not communicate with other parts of the building; access should be from the outside, by outward opening doors (which can be secured open when people are working inside). They should be at ground level, used just for chlorine storage, secure and restricted to authorised personnel.

The store's size should be related to the minimum number of full standy, on-line and empty cylinders needed to operate the installation, allowing room for normal maintenance only. For a single cylinder installation, a room about 2 by 1.25m is sufficient. If pipes or ducts must pass through the store, all passages through the walls must be securely sealed against leaks. The floor should be level. A minimum temperature of about 13°C is recommended for an adequate flow of gas, maintained by hot water heated coil, non-radiant heater or radiator; cylinders must be kept below 50°C. Waterproof and sealed mains light and emergency lighting must be fitted.

Leak control The vacuum system now preferred for new installations operates with a completely sealed gas cylinder storage area, with an air-tight door and a water fogging device to deal with leaks. Chlorine detectors and alarms are still provided. The detector should alarm at 3-5ppm - as a warning; higher levels activate the sprays. The water sprays come from a number of fogged nozzles mounted on the store ceiling. The system needs a strainer prior to the nozzles, and weekly checks. The water dissolves the gas and there is a drain to a sump for subsequent safe disposal.

Securing cylinders Clamps, chains, bars or battened framing should be provided. Caps or domes, as appropriate, must be fitted to the empty cylinders which must be clearly marked 'empty' and secured upright as for full cylinders.

Sodium hypochlorite

Containers of sodium hypochlorite must be kept apart from those of hydrochloric acid and sodium bisulphate - because of the violent reactions (releasing chlorine gas) between the two types of chemical.

- Each pool chemical should be labelled and have its own bund and sump.
- Bulk storage tanks should have a sump. It must be possible to empty the sump safely - usually by transfer pump. It must be resistant to attack from acid and alkali, and not connected directly to a sewer or surface water drain. (Emptying sumps to main sewers after spillages requires the permission of the relevant water authority.)
- Bunds can be brick (or concrete block), rendered, and with a chemically resistant lining (perhaps tiles); or a plastic resistant to the chemical being stored.
- The partitions between adjacent bunds should be at least 800mm high. Acids and alkalis (including hypochlorites) must not be in adjacent bunds - ideally, not in the same store room.
- The volume of the bund must be at least

50% of the total capacity of the maximum number of containers stored at any one time.

- The bund should be capable of holding 110% of the contents of the largest container within it.
- The height of the bund wall and its distance from containers should be enough to contain a jet of liquid from a puncture.
- These considerations about the size of bunds should also take into account the weight of containers being lifted over bund walls. (Special lifting arrangements may be necessary.) The planned height of bund walls can often be reduced by increasing the overall internal area of the bund.

Storage space should be big enough to take two months' stock (one month full, one month empty) - though, ideally, less may be stored, depending on availability, etc. The suppliers' advice on storage should be followed. For ease of handling, containers should be of about 20 litres nominal capacity, fitted with lifting points or handles.

If sodium hypochlorite has to be transferred from one container to another, a transfer pump is recommended; pouring the liquid is unsafe.

Bulk storage   A month's supply of at least 1 cubic metre (1,000l in a 1,500l tank) is the smallest capacity that is economical for bulk storage. A conventional 25-metre pool is likely to need a 1,500-litre tank, with deliveries of about 1,000 litres. A typical tank would be constructed from 7mm-thick black polyethylene, with a flat base and top and a sealed manhole. It would have 50mm bore vent and overflow lines, 40mm diameter washout connection with cap, 20mm diameter outlet connection to day tank (with ball valve), float type level indicator, and 40mm diameter fill line with diaphragm valve and a lockable, tamperproof fitting at the fill point that mates with the delivery vehicle fitting.

The tank should be securely located on a plinth, allowing gravity feed to day tank(s); clearly labelled with details of its contents and warnings.

Each pool supplied by the bulk tank should have a plastic day tank sized for at least 2 days' supply. These should have connections for an air vent/overflow, an outlet for dosing pump connection and an inlet from the bulk tank. If the day tank is at a lower level than the bulk tank, in the same bund, the transfer can be driven by gravity, with a valve accessible from outside the bund.

The pipes between bulk and day tanks should be rigid, securely fixed and have labelled valves. Access to valves should be easy and safe. A strainer should be fitted so that delivery to the day tank is clean. Cleaning the in-line filter should be possible without draining down.

Bulk tanks should be inspected after five years, and annually thereafter. Welds are vulnerable and embrittlement a possibility. They should never be subject to mechanical shock.

Calcium hypochlorite
There should be storage for a maximum of 2 months' supply. The containers are designed to be stacked no more than two high. If there is an automatic mixing system linked to the main circulation, it should be within a bund and there should be an overflow alarm.

Chapter 19

Heating and air circulation

Maintaining satisfactory environmental conditions in the pool hall and all other areas of the building is essential for the comfort of bathers, lifeguards, staff, spectators, teachers, etc - and for the pool to operate successfully over a reasonably extended working life.

The heating of the pool water, and the heating and ventilation of the pool hall, need to take into account a wide range of factors such as bathing load, water temperature and quality; plant room location; integration with the building structure; materials and insulation of the pool hall envelope; capital, operating and life cycle costs.

Then the temperature of the air and the water need to be linked and balanced so as to get the right humidity, optimise user comfort and minimise evaporation from the pool water. It is also necessary to ensure that the air circulation system distributes the air effectively over the whole of the pool hall area.

POOL WATER HEATING

The actual heating of the pool water is a relatively simple operation. It is generally carried out by a heat exchanger (normally a low-pressure hot water system at 82°C flow, 71°C return) to transfer heat from the primary heating system, sometimes via heat recovery systems, to the pool water. The heater is generally sized on the basis of raising the pool water temperature by 0.5°C per hour (to adjust temperature, make good heat lost by evaporation, backwashing, etc). If a pool is being heated from cold, the rate must be no more than 0.25°C per hour, otherwise rates of expansion of materials may cause problems to the pool structure or lining. Particularly on a new pool, the precise rate of temperature rise should be determined by its designers.

The heating control system must be capable of coping accurately with a wide range of temperatures. It may be possible, through the use of mixing valves and associated equipment, to serve different pools at different temperatures from a single heat exchanger. But it is recommended that a separate heat exchanger and controls are provided for each separate pool water area (so they can have different temperatures) - unless the pools share one filtration and circulation system.

Temperatures

There has been a consistent trend towards higher water temperatures in recent years, encouraged by the substantial growth in leisure pools and special swimming sessions for young children. In 1984 government guidelines on pool water remarked that water temperatures were then increasing to as high as 27°C. Similar temperatures 10 years or so later would be regarded as quite low: main pool temperatures appear to be commonly around 29°C and even 30°C and above in some instances.

Some pools do need to be this warm - eg for parents and toddlers. But operators tempted to join the move towards higher temperatures should bear in mind that they do create a number of problems.

- Microorganisms multiply faster - up to twice as fast for a 10°C rise; filters are increasingly likely to become colonised.
- Bathers get hotter - limiting serious swimming and increasing sweat and grease in the water.
- Energy costs, direct and indirect, are higher - whatever efficiency or conservation methods are used.
- Air temperatures, which are linked to those of the water, rise too - making the atmosphere less comfortable for staff and others (as can the higher moisture levels).
- There is more moisture in the pool atmosphere, even when relative humidity is controlled at the same level - with a risk of condensation and possibly corrosion and deterioration of the building fabric, structure and equipment.
- Dissolved gases become less soluble - more

bad smells (chloramines) and potentially harmful haloforms; plus pH value rises as carbon dioxide escapes.

With an increasingly wide variety of pool uses, and operators attempting to introduce more flexibility into programming of pool operation, it is obviously difficult to select a single appropriate or optimum operating temperature for any particular pool. The large volumes of water involved make it impossible to vary water temperatures rapidly in any one water area. This means that the selection and accurate control of the optimum water temperature for each pool is essential.

The temperature of the pool hall air should normally be maintained at around the water temperature - no more than 1 degree C above or below. But it is recommended that air temperatures of 30°C or more should generally be avoided. Clearly there may have to be compromises where, for example, mothers and toddlers have to be accommodated in the same area as fitness swimming.

Recommended maximum pool water temperatures

Competitive swimming and diving, fitness swimming, training	27°C
Recreational, adult teaching, conventional main pools	28°C
Children's teaching, leisure pools	29°C
Babies, young children, disabled	30°C

VENTILATION, AIR CIRCULATION

This is a complex and critical area. It is generally recommended that air is well distributed over the whole area, and that air movement within the occupied zone is maintained within acceptable conditions for bather comfort.

The ventilation system is normally the primary, or only means of:
- removing chlorinous smells and other disinfection byproducts and contaminants (including trihalomethanes) from the air
- controlling the pool hall air quality, temperature and humidity and hence evaporation from the pool surface
- preventing condensation
- maintaining comfortable environmental conditions, including relatively draught-free conditions for bathers.

The ideal ventilation rate for a pool hall, taking into account varying external conditions, bathing loads, evaporation rate, water quality, etc is very difficult to estimate and will, by necessity, change with varying circumstances.

An effective, well distributed mechanical supply and extract ventilation system is, however, essential to maintain satisfactory internal environmental conditions under all potential variations. It is almost inevitable that there will be disinfection byproducts in the water and thus the air directly above the pool water. To replace this with fresh air is likely to demand some direct extraction of byproducts or supply of air over the pool - but ideally without causing draughts.

A recommended guideline figure of 10 litres of ventilation air per second per m² of total pool hall area (water area plus all wet surrounds) has proven to be acceptable in a wide range of pools. This should also maintain a satisfactory humidity.

This normally results in an overall total of approximately 4 to 6 air changes per hour depending on the height of the pool hall, but this may need to be increased to 8 or 10 for leisure pools with extensive water features.

It is generally recommended that the relative humidity is maintained between 50% and 70% throughout the pool hall area (recommended control level of 60%±10%). Levels above 70% produce a risk of discomfort and condensation, and levels lower than 50% can increase evaporation and energy use.

Humidification control (using de-humidifiers, etc) can help control pool hall conditions, but this does not replace the need for adequate ventilation to control air quality.

Separate areas
Areas for eating, drinking, etc within the pool building are a potential problem. Their individual requirements should be assessed carefully. Those areas do not necessarily need to be physically separated from the pool hall, but environmental conditions different from those around the pool must be considered.

Sources of ventilation
The best source for ventilation is fresh air; this should be the first consideration for all pools.

There should, at all times, be a minimum of 12 litres per second of fresh air provided for each occupant of the pool hall (bathers, staff, spectators, etc). If recirculation is used for energy efficiency, a 30% minimum of fresh air should be provided; with 100% fresh air available when necessary (eg very high bather loads and/or high levels of contaminants in the pool atmosphere). The appropriate building regulations should be consulted.

Recirculation of pool air produces a risk of increased build-up of contaminants in the pool environment. This can aggravate respiratory complaints, especially in staff. It also increases the potential for deterioration in equipment and components made of metal or nylon - structural steelwork, roof and ceiling fittings, air handling plant and equipment, etc. Any recirculation introduced should, therefore, be carefully controlled - for example, restricted to periods when pool covers are in use to reduce evaporation.

ENERGY MANAGEMENT

Swimming pools are one of the few building types operating at such high temperature and humidity throughout the year. This results in potentially high heat losses and means that all pool buildings should be well insulated - above basic building regulation standards if possible. And they should be well sealed from the outside and surrounding areas.

Heating the ventilation air will generally be one of the major energy loads for a pool. So a simple heat exchange device such as a plate heat exchanger or run-around coils should generally be provided to reclaim as much energy as possible from the exhaust air, in order to optimise energy efficiency.

Other energy efficiency devices can be considered, such as thermal wheels, heat pumps, desiccant wheels and combined heat and power units - but these should be carefully evaluated over the projected life cycle of the building services installation.

The ventilation system should operate all the time the pool is in use, and it may be needed even when the pool is not in use, to maintain environmental conditions within the pool hall and prevent condensation. An effective pool cover can normally reduce the need for the

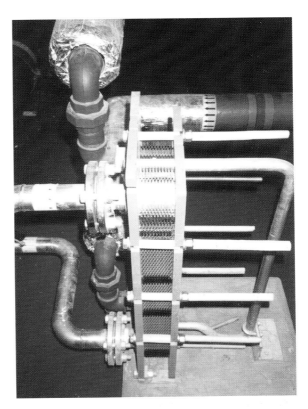

Heat exchanger

ventilation system to operate at full loading out of hours (it may even allow it to be shut off) and therefore substantially reduce energy use.

There are more details of heating and air circulation in pools in the Sports Council's *Handbook of Sports and Recreational Building Design Vol III* (see Bibliography). For further guidance on energy management, the Building Research Establishment Energy Conservation Support Unit (BRECSU) has a series of publications.

Chapter 20

Management and training

Swimming or simply bathing in pool water should be a healthy and pleasant exercise. A clear, safe, sparkling swimming pool without unpleasant smell or taste is the right of every swimmer and should be the objective of every manager. But achieving this in practice can be fraught with difficulty. A multitude of physical, chemical and microbiological states change in a busy swimming pool - some in seconds, others in hours or days. Only a trained pool operator can identify, understand and manage these.

There are many factors critical to pool water quality that are studied in more detail elsewhere in this book.

- **Human contamination** Skin, hair, throat and faecal bacteria, body oils, cosmetics, ammonia and nitrogenous matter from sweat and urine, dirt, food, saliva, open infections.
- **Environmental** Source water quality, physical and chemical composition of pool water, algae and fungi, gases formed from chemical reactions, air and water temperatures, air quality and pollution, humidity, sunlight, evaporation.
- **Design, construction and operation** Pool bathing load, turnover, construction materials, dilution, hydraulics, chemical conditioning, disinfectants, dosing control, coagulants, filtration, testing and ventilation.

Given these factors - any of which can affect bathing conditions and become a hazard to health - a pool requires proactive management.

MANAGEMENT STRUCTURE

The actual management structure will vary according to the type of facility. A small community pool will probably require a small nucleus of multi-skilled staff trained to understand and interpret swimming pool water conditions. This team should be trained in the plant room techniques required to maintain

water quality, under the guidance of a pool manager qualified both professionally and by experience. In this scale of facility it is not cost effective to employ specialist engineers and plant room technicians, but this does not mean that water quality control should be neglected. Staff with hands-on competence are ideal. But as the size and complexity of the pool increases, it becomes more appropriate to specialise. In a large, multi-facility site, with major capital investment in engineering plant and controls, the services of a qualified and experienced engineer or plant technician are indispensable. But understanding the pool water treatment process should not stop with the appointment of an engineer. The actions of lifeguards, supervisors and managers also have an effect on the pool water. So they should all understand the basic chemistry and microbiology of pool water treatment, and the plant room and pool procedures that maintain good water quality.

The lifeguard has to understand the need for a hygienic pool area, the importance of pre-swim hygiene and what action to take in a soiling incident. The supervisor should be sufficiently familiar with water quality to be able to correct a condition which could lead to deterioration. If for whatever reason pool water begins to lose clarity, the on-site supervisor must be able to decide if bathing should cease.

Managers responsible for a range of sport and recreational facilities will delegate much of the day-to-day functioning of individual specialist areas (like pools) to team members with the appropriate skills. Nevertheless, the manager still carries the ultimate responsibility. Whether or not managers have hands-on skills (ideally they should) they must understand how things work. This concept can be applied to all managers, but in the context of a swimming pool it has a special significance. Simply, there is a lot that can go wrong.

- Water can be a vehicle for the transmission of disease - see Chapter 14. Many microorganisms prefer a warm, moist environment with an adequate food source - perfectly provided in a swimming pool with poorly maintained water.

■ Careless management of coagulation, filtration, disinfection and chemical balance can produce a degree of turbidity (cloudiness) that obscures swimmers' and lifeguards' vision of the pool bottom, even in shallow water. Each year around 11 people drown in UK pools, some partly as a result of unclear water.

HEALTH AND SAFETY

The manager or pool operator is responsible under the Health and Safety at Work, Etc Act 1974 to ensure, so far as is reasonably practicable, the health and safety of employees at work and others who may be affected by the undertaking. This includes protecting the public who use a swimming pool. The manager must have the necessary authority to implement such measures as are reasonable to ensure the premises are safe and that all plant is operated, and substances stored and used, safely without risks to health.

The Health & Safety Executive book, *Management of Health and Safety in Swimming Pools*, deals with management responsibility for swimming pool water treatment. (See Bibliography, page 138.) Although this is only a guidance document, the extent of its application should not be underestimated. It is the standard that will be used by a health and safety inspector or environmental health officer when making an inspection or carrying out an investigation. It can be, and is, quoted in a court of law. *Management of Health and Safety in Swimming Pools* guidance has the weight and effectiveness of legislation without the jargon. Moreover, that book explicitly relies on this one for the detail of pool water treatment. A manager of a swimming pool clearly has specific responsibilities for health and safety which are a legal requirement. So all such managers must understand the principles and processes involved.

Managers discharge their responsibility by identifying the hazards and then by taking precautions to control the risks. Training, certification and record keeping are fundamental in providing a safe, healthy environment and are the manager's key to safeguarding legal requirements and a successful operation.

COSHH

The Control of Substances Hazardous to Health Regulations 1994 (COSHH) apply to employers whose business involves 'substances hazardous to health' - which includes all disinfectants and other chemicals used in and around a swimming pool. Employers must have copies of the relevant legislation on the premises. They must first make a formal assessment of the health risks to employees and anybody using the premises; also of the measures needed to protect these people's health. This assessment must be regularly reviewed and updated if circumstances change - eg a change of disinfectant, cleaning chemicals, or method of application.

There is a responsibility on employers to use the 'least hazardous' chemical that gives satisfactory performance. This requirement is worth serious consideration when choosing disinfectants and other pool water treatment chemicals, and when doing a risk assessment. The declared hazards of pool chemicals, and how this relates to risk assessment, is discussed in Chapter 16.

'Substances hazardous to health' can also include microorganisms, byproducts and any substances which create the sort of hazard to health that a classified chemical might. So pool operators should include in their COSHH assessment specific consideration of bacteria and viruses, other pollutants, disinfection byproducts etc.

As COSHH applies to microbiological safety, pool managers have a clear responsibility to assess the exposure and deal with it through disinfection. This demands microbiological testing (detailed in Chapter 15). The responsibility for ensuring compliance with regulations in school and local authority pools lies with the Health & Safety Executive. Privately owned (not domestic) pools - hotel, holiday camp, etc - are dealt with by local authority environment health departments and officers (EHOs). Although EHOs have the right of entry to any pool open to the public (under the Environmental Protection Act 1990) and of doing microbiological tests if they think it necessary, this does not take away the manager's responsibility for regular testing.

OPERATIONAL CONSIDERATIONS

With increasing demands on public expenditure, the competitive tendering of public services and increased awareness of conservation issues, there is pressure to find more cost-effective ways of operating swimming pools. The costs of water, energy, water treatment and disposal of waste water are very real concerns for managers; but where the consequences of alterations and adaptations to limit these costs are not fully understood, disaster can follow.

Ill-informed application of possibly inappropriate energy conservation and water treatment systems may well increase the cost of operations dramatically and require the early replacement of major items of plant, equipment and buildings. Closure may even result.

In terms of capital expenditure, energy, maintenance and day-to-day operation, a swimming pool is an expensive item. Pool buildings are designed and constructed with a probable life expectancy of 50 to 60 years (but only about 20 for some engineering services). Managers and staff must be trained to obtain maximum life from their facilities and to operate them cost effectively.

Poor maintenance and operation can be attributed to a lack of professional expertise or knowledge (or possibly resources). Either way, it represents a failure of management. And it may lead to the owners of pools, local authorities, schools or private operators being forced to spend huge sums on pool refurbishment, new filters, plumbing, pumps, tiling, grouting, calorifiers, steelwork in the pool hall, heating and ventilation plant, lighting and electrics - often after less than ten years' operation.

TRAINING

The key person dealing with health, safety and cost issues in a swimming pool is the manager. A manager who is trained, qualified and competent in swimming pool operation is a fundamental requirement. There are simply too many things that can go wrong in a swimming pool for it to be managed and operated by untrained staff. The providers of all non-domestic swimming pools should be expected to ensure that their managers and staff are appropriately trained.

National vocational qualifications are currently being developed for those responsible for plant operation, up to supervisory level. Their application at more senior levels would be desirable; ideally, a qualification based on an assessment of competence in the work place will be available at all levels in the pool staffing hierarchy. There is also a need for a nationally recognised and applied qualification for pool lifeguards.

There are a number of sources for training. The Institute of Sport & Recreation Management (ISRM) has trained managers and staff for more than 70 years. Its training programmes and qualifications are recognised by the Department for Education & Employment under the 1992 Further & Higher Education Act, the local authority associations, the Local Government Management Board, the Health & Safety Executive and Sport England (Sports Council as was). ISRM provides training at four levels, generally delivered over two years in the form of day-release courses at colleges throughout the UK or distance learning with UNISON. The Institute of Leisure & Amenity Management (ILAM) is a more recent arrival on the training scene. Addresses are on page 137.

The Management of Health and Safety at Work Regulations and the COSHH process includes the need for staff involved in the handling and use of chemicals to receive appropriate training and instruction. Even the most thorough COSHH arangements will fail unless all employees are aware of the risks associated with their work and how these risks may be avoided. This training must include enough knowledge and understanding of the chemicals for staff to be alert to any changes affecting safety. Managers must ensure such training is done.

Staff training, and clear, written procedures distributed to all employees, should include:
- safety requirements
- labelling and safety notices
- signs on site
- material safety data sheets (maintained on site) for all chemicals used
- information on delivery, storage, handling and use.

A typical log sheet

SWIMMING POOL LOG SHEET - MONDAY / / TO SUNDAY / /			MON			TUE			WED			THUR			FRI			SAT			SUN		
Water Pumps																								
Pump Started Time																								
Pump Stopped Time																								
Hours Running																								
Pump In Use No.1, 2 or 3																								
Strainers Changed																								
Filters			IN	OUT		IN	OUT		IN	OUT		IN	OUT		IN	OUT		IN	OUT		IN	OUT		
Inlet And Outlet Pressures	No. 1																							
	No. 2																							
	No. 3																							
	No. 4																							
Backwash (Mins)	No. 1																							
	No. 2																							
	No. 3																							
	No. 4																							
Circulation Flow M³/h or l/h																								
Test Results		Fr	Co	pH	Fr	Co	pH	Fr	Co	pH	Fr	Co	pH	Fr	Co	pH	Fr	Co	pH	Fr	Co	pH		
FREE, COMBINED CHLORINE & pH	Test 1																							
	Test 2																							
	Test 3																							
	Test 4																							
	Test 5																							
	Test 6																							
	Test 7																							
	Test 8																							
Analysis of Monochloramine Dichloramine		M	Di		M	Di		M	Di		M	Di		M	Di		M	Di		M	Di			
	Test																							
	Test																							
Total Alkalinity																								
Calcium Hardness																								
Total Dissolved Solids																								
Temperature																								
Langelier Index																								
CHEMICAL ADDITIONS	Alum/ Coagulant																							
	Hypochlorite																							
	CO_2/Acid																							
	Others																							
	Others																							
Clarity 10=Perfect 0=V.Poor																								
Number of Bathers																								
Fresh Water Dilution (Litres)																								

Managers should check that staff understand and follow all procedures and are aware of their responsibilities. Monitoring and review of the arrangements and their effectiveness must then follow. Actual training sessions need to be recorded and reviewed.

To sum up, information, instruction and training are the key requirements for all staff involved in the storage, handling and use of swimming pool chemicals.

How much training

The amount of training that staff responsible for swimming pool water must undertake is related to their responsibilites and the success of the training programme. Pool staff, for example, who need to understand the influences on pool water quality - especially related to hygiene and customer service - should ideally have some general awareness and knowledge. The extent of that knowledge should be enough to ensure safety and hygiene - from what chemicals are safe to use on the poolside to what to do about a severe nose bleed in the pool. If their duties are to include water testing, their training must expand accordingly. It should be possible to achieve these objectives in eight hours or so with an experienced trainer.

A pool manager's knowledge must be broad enough to manage a pool successfully - to make the difference between a good pool and a bad one, between safety and hazard, economic success and financial disaster. This means managing staff and dealing with specialist contractors. A good manager will be comfortable with most of the contents of this book, at training new staff and writing technical specifications for a new pool.

Staff responsible for plant operation must have hands-on skills - not the breadth of knowledge of managers, but the ability to interpret from pool conditions what responses are needed in the plant room. They must carry the responsibility for handling chemicals safely. A minimum of 21 hours' training is recommended, together with a work-related exercise to demonstrate specific knowledge of their own workplace.

REGULATION

The publications listed in the Bibliography, like this book, are advisory not mandatory. Much of their guidance is intended to assist those responsible to meet the requirements of the Health and Safety at Work, Etc Act 1974. Operators at pools are strongly advised to consult all appropriate publications. In general, in the event of an accident, the more closely operators have followed accepted guidelines, the less vulnerable they are to a successful action for public liability through negligence, or any other legal action.

For new disinfection systems or conversions, co-operation and consultation is essential - among architects, engineers, water treatment equipment and chemical suppliers, pool managers and operators and environmental health officers, before the design is finalised. (See Chapter 3.) In some circumstances it may be advisable to consult also the Health and Safety Executive locally.

Chapter 21

Plant maintenance

Water treatment, like any mechanical system, requires regular inspection and maintenance to ensure continuous efficient operation. Full details for all three should be incorporated into the system's Operations and Maintenance (O&M) manual.

Inspection starts with the system installation and its commissioning; it continues, with maintenance, throughout the life of the pool and its plant. The details will be specific to the plant - but the lists that follow give some idea of the range of checks that will need to be made. All procedures should be incorporated in printed charts that can be followed and completed (then filed) by inspection and maintenance personnel.

DESIGN VERIFICATION

The first part of the O&M manual should incorporate the key details of the design and the equipment. The specification of the various parameters should be logged alongside how each has been calculated, and what the actual values are.

General parameters
Pool capacity
Turnover period
Hourly flow
Total flow rate of system
Filter area
Filtration rate
Number and size of filters
Backwash rate and backwash flow
Filter inlet pressure (mean)
Filter outlet pressure (mean)
Pool temperature (mean)
Pool pH value (manual reading)
Pool chlorine (manual reading)
Plant room temperature
Plant room humidity
Ozone system details
UV system details
Valve settings

Chemical equipment details
Controller type
Chlorine donor and set point
Acid or alkali donor
pH value set point
Coagulant
Solution strengths
Dosage rates
Dosing pump outputs

Pumps and air blowers
Duty
Motor size

MAINTENANCE

A typical maintenance schedule is given here for filtration plant and dosing equipment, as an example of the right approach. Maintenance should be planned on a programmed basis, based on detailed knowledge of all items of equipment. The mechanism for this may be anything from cards to computers. All items listed should be checked at least once a year; some - see next section - as often as weekly.

Filtration plant maintenance
For each filter:
- clean pressure gauge connections (inlet and outlet) and check gauges read correctly
- strip down and clean bulk and auto air release systems; check operations
- check and clean sight glass
- inspect filter lining at and above sand level; if filter is open, take a sand sample for checking.

A carbon filter (ozone reaction vessel) would demand the same - with particular attention to the state of the carbon and the vessel lining.

For each valve:
- check isolating valves operate correctly in the opened and closed position
- check non-returning valves seal correctly in the closed position
- detail any problems with valves.

For each pump:
- check mechanical seal for leakage
- check bearings (grease if necessary)
- check for hot or noisy running
- check for excess vibration
- take pressure gauge readings at various flows
- check line current of motor at various flows.

Air scour and air blower systems; compressor/receiver systems - check:
- bearings (grease if necessary)
- hot or noisy running
- excess vibration
- air filters, silencers, etc
- oil level (fill if necessary)
- pressure gauge readings
- drainage of receiver unit (moisture in solenoid valves).

Pool heating calorifiers:
- check pool heat exchangers for leakage
- record positions of inlet/outlet and bypass valves.

Pipework system:
- check visually for leaks and support brackets, etc
- tighten joints (refix brackets as necessary).

Ozone unit maintenance is an area best left to specialists (who should work to a detailed checklist).

Dosing equipment maintenance

This requires special attention because of the hazardous nature of the chemicals involved. Maintenance personnel must be aware of which chemicals are involved, and be familiar with COSHH sheets and safety precautions. They must work to procedures drawn up by experienced people and approved by management; they must be appropriately trained. Every piece of equipment must be checked at least every six months, with an annual overhaul; replacement may be necessary within five to ten years. Probes for chlorine and pH can need replacing every year, but their deterioration can be detected by a slowing of response.

Dosing systems have the following specific requirements.
- Any part that needs maintenance must be acessible - and kept that way.
- Chemical systems need regular

preventative maintenance - rather than repair on breakdown. This is cheaper in the long run.
- With hazardous chemicals, the whole system must be depressurised and flushed out with water before work can start on it.
- Only replacement parts supplied by the manufacturer (or approved by them) should be used. The use of non-specified tubing, for example - though it may appear satisfactory - will void manufacturers' liabilities as it may not seal adequately, and could cause an accident. (For example, nylon used where polyethylene tubing has been specified may become brittle or even dissolve.)
- If parts are returned to manufacturers for repair, they must first be thoroughly washed to remove chemical contamination, or be accompanied by COSHH sheets for the particular chemical.
- Sufficient spares (as recommended by the manufacturer) should be kept for routine replacement and in case of failure.
- A standby dosing pump should be considered, if the pool has to be kept running in the event of pump breakdown (and hand dosing is not an alternative).
- Regular removal of scale on injection fittings (for example) may be necessary; it may involve mechanical and then chemical cleaning. Such parts should be removed from the system and washed first.

A YEAR IN THE LIFE...

Routine servicing and maintenance is likely to follow something like the pattern below. Some items may need to be done more often. (A general caution: oil should be kept well away from pool chemicals.)

Daily checks (and possible adjustments)
Levels of hypochlorite and acid in day tanks
Level in alum solution tank or PAC day tank
Pool levels
Water testing (typically three times a day)

Weekly service
Backwash filters (maybe more frequently)
Inspect and clean strainer boxes
Check air intake element is free from dirt on air blowers
Rotate duty/standby pumping units
Clean ozone generator tops and surrounds
Backwash carbon deozonising filters

Check oil levels and condensate in compressor and air blower (drain)
Check calibration of dosing control unit
Plant flow rate (clean indicator plant pot and internal orifice plate)
Manual air release valves (clean strainers, automatic air release valves; correct faults on suction side filtration system)
Check in-line strainers on the dosing pump suction side and on filter air release (clean)
Water levels in anti-syphon catchpots from ozoniser and destructor (top up)
Ozone generator intakes
Dust ozone generator

Monthly
Check glands or mechanical seals of all pumping units
Check in-line strainer on alum pump suction
Check air intake filter and belt tension on compressor
Drain, clean and flush out deck-level channels
Check automatic chemical control equipment against buffers
Check deozonising carbon
Dust down all motors, etc

Every 6-12 months
Full check on chemical control system
Inspect condition of filtration media and lining
Verify adherence to manufacturers' technical information and service contract
Compressor: clean outside and check inlet/discharge valves (replace?)
Balance and holding tanks are drained and cleaned twice a year
Check carbon level in deozonisers (top up; replace annually)
Check seals and valves on ozone system

FAULT FINDING

Pool plant faults are due either to incorrect operation or to plant failure - so instructions must be followed; short cuts banned. But a few typical problems and solutions are worth outlining. (See Problem sorter, page 134 for general pool water problems.)

Air discharge at pool inlet
The bulk air release may be blocked - check:
- strainers at bulk air release mechanisms
- that pipe to backwash line is clear
- operation of air release valve.

Sand at pool inlets
- Incorrect backwashing - refer to operating instructions.
- It may indicate a broken nozzle or filter lateral.

Circulation pump output low
The in-line strainer may be blocked. Or the valves may be incorrectly set:
- check pressure gauge
- check suction and discharge valves and pump are open
- check filter frontal valves for correct setting - are inlet and filter outlet open?
- filter backwashing may be required.

Pressure differential high after backwashing time allowed for backwash
The filter may still be dirty - not enough time backwashing. Or backwashing may have been done other than according to instructions. Or the media bed may be heavily soiled: repeat backwash if possible. Check gauges, air scour, backwash flow rate.

Chapter 22

Cleaning

Like anywhere used by a large number of people, the building housing a swimming pool must be kept clean. Many of the issues that arise are common to all such public places; but because of the importance of maintaining good pool water quality, there are special considerations involved.

Any outside dirt that gets into the pool - either more or less directly from shoes around a leisure or outdoor pool, or via changing room floors - will add to the burden on water treatment. Conversely, the injudicious use of cleaners (especially those containing unsuitable surfactants) can add further to this burden, as well as affecting disinfection, pH control and chemical monitoring. No cleaning should be undertaken without a full knowledge of the water treatment system, the cleaner, and how the two might interact.

Chapter 4 deals with pre-swim hygiene, (showers, toilets, footbaths, changing rooms). This chapter deals with cleansing generally - of the pool and the pool hall.

IN AND AROUND THE POOL

Although the transmission of foot infections in swimming pools arouses less anxiety than it once did, floor surfaces should be kept clean. Dirt from shoes should be controlled by good changing room design. Floors should be thoroughly cleansed once each day by a combination of hosing, mopping and scrubbing.

Cleaning around the pool is more tricky, as it is virtually impossible to keep cleaning products out of the water - particularly if the pool is deck-level (the water level with the surround). And almost any chemical cleaner will have an effect on pool water and its proper treatment. This can start when the pool is new and cleaners are used to remove building stains and to disinfect surfaces. The products of such cleaning should all be flushed to drain before final filling and commissioning. If not, there may be strange residual readings on start up. If, for example, a chlorinated isocyanurate cleaner was used, and the pool operator did not know, it could be difficult to explain why the DPD no 1 test might give one figure for free chlorine and the chlorine analyser for free chlorine a different one.

Pool surrounds should be cleaned daily by washing and scrubbing with pool water only. Ideally, there should be some way of draining all poolside washings outside the building. Deposits of dirt etc just above the water line can be cleaned off with a chemical-free scouring pad, using sodium bicarbonate or carbonate solution. (Operators should wear gloves and goggles.)

If daily cleaning does not get the pool surrounds clean, the residue should not be left so long it becomes stubborn. Proprietary chemical cleaners, if required, should be formulated for poolside use, and come from reputable suppliers. But even reputable suppliers may not be aware of the potential problems cleaners that are suitable for, say, a hospital can cause in pool water treatment and analysis. For example, they may contain surfactants which can affect the monitoring of chlorine residual. They may contain oxidising agents which give a false reading on DPD tests but not necessarily on the automatic analyser. Other compounds simply contain ammonia (they may smell of it) and could produce unhealthy pool conditions. The offending constituent may not be considered hazardous, and may not even be the main ingredient. Ammonium salts of organic substances like vegetable oils, for example, are often included. Others are simply based on hydrochloric acid in an inert, viscous carrier and may therefore be suitable. But the presence of a fresh pine odour indicates a product to be avoided, even if the other ingredients seem inoffensive

Of course, care should be taken to avoid outright incompatability between cleaners and pool chemicals, which could be dangerous. (The chlorinated isocyanurates, especially, can react violently with hypochlorites; in general, reactions between acid and alkalis are potentially explosive.) With deck-level pools, it should be possible to isolate the balance tank system and empty it to drain, to stop cleaning chemicals' entering the pool.

Either way, the use of cleaners should be strictly controlled, and any possible contamination of the pool monitored. Pools should never be cleaned when there are people in the pool.

The underside of pool covers should be checked regularly for contamination and algal growth, and cleaned as necessary.

Channels and balance tanks

About once a month deck-level transfer channels should be drained (by lowering the pool water level marginally). The channels can then be cleaned by flushing out with 10mg/l chlorinated water which can return to the balance tank. A correctly designed balance tank should clear most debris continuously. In this case it need be drained only twice a year, any debris cleared out and its inner surfaces brushed and flushed down with 10mg/l chlorinated water that can be returned to the circulation system via the filters. Fumes may be a problem for the person cleaning the tank. So, too, is a balance tank that has not been designed for such access. Nobody should enter a balance tank alone. Tanks and channels should be checked monthly for any build-up of debris: sand, for example, can be a sign of concrete deterioration - as well as a home for bacteria which may then spread to other parts of the pool. Calcium deposits may suggest poor chemical balance.

THE BOTTOM OF THE POOL

No pool floor has a slope steep enough to make it self-cleaning. So there must be some means of regularly removing debris, algae etc - even if only sweeping it towards the deepest outlet grating using a wide, weighted brush with long handle attachments. Suction will be needed to clear algae and other staining from the sides and bottom. Deck-level pools need to be suction cleaned daily. In general, bottom cleaning should be done regularly enough to avoid big algal problems - particularly common with pools running at the higher

temperatures often found over recent years.

Most mobile suction sweepers have their own power unit. All electrical systems should comply with the Electricity at Work Regulations 1989 and the current IEE Regulations. Those sweepers relying on direct connection to the mains water supply are likely to contravene local water by-laws.

More sophisticated pool bottom cleaners are radio controlled or programmed in some way to cover the whole of the bottom systematically. Some will pump out through the pool's filtration system; many have built-in filters.

TILES

There is an authoritative publication covering the cleaning of ceramic and quarry tiles - *The Cleaning of Ceramic Tiles*, free from the British Ceramic Tile Council (phone 01782 747147). Acid washing may be necessary to get the tiles clean; the manufacturer's advice should be sought first.

MOVEABLE FLOORS

If the design allows, moveable floors may be brought to the surface and tilted (with great care) so that both surfaces can be cleaned. If not, specialist divers will be needed, who should work to the Diving at Work Regulations 1997.

EMPTYING THE POOL

A pool should not be emptied unless absolutely necessary, and never without taking expert advice, as enormous damage can be done to the structure. (There is a British Standard and an ISRM code of practice on this - see Bibliography.) Operators should notify the relevant water authorities about the discharge and refilling (see page 12). Whenever a pool is emptied, the bottom and sides should be scrubbed if necessary. If a detergent or strong disinfectant is used, it should be flushed thoroughly to drain before the pool is refilled.

Chapter 23

Protection and first aid

There are nearly 1,000 injuries recorded each year in UK swimming pools. Over two-thirds involve falling, being struck by something or bumping into something. About 40 injuries arise from handling, lifting or carrying. Only about 15 involved exposure to the sort of harmful substances found in stores and plant rooms. But most of those were major injuries, so such risks demand proper protection.

However strict and well worked out the procedures are for delivery, storage and use of disinfectant and other chemicals, there is a need for protective clothing and other equipment - and, in case of accidents despite all this, good first aid backup. (Appropriate first aid should also be available for the public.)

All such equipment should be stored on purpose-designed shelves, hooks, etc, in a clearly identified area. Training in its use should be given and updated as necessary.

PERSONAL PROTECTION

The Personal Protective Equipment Regulations 1992 require pool operators to assess and provide necessary personal protective equipment (PPE) when performing certain tasks. Pool operators are recommended (by the Health & Safety Executive) to take suppliers' advice about this. But wherever in the pool building there is a foreseeable risk of contamination from chemicals, protective clothing should be available. This must be impervious to the chemicals that could be encountered. It might consist of dust masks and face protection; goggles or face-shields; hard-toe rubber boots; overalls supplemented by full-length aprons of rubber or acid-resistant plastic; rubber elbow-length industrial gloves; respirator mask for vapour and dust.

Gloves and eye protection should be worn however small a quantity of chemical is being handled.

CANISTER RESPIRATORS

Where liquid disinfectant is stored in bulk, or with chlorine plants, canister respirators rated for chlorine should be available. They are designed only for minor leakages (under 1% by volume). Serious leaks, or a shortage of oxygen, demand self-contained breathing apparatus and fully trained personnel - usually fire authorities. Respirators should also be able to protect against particles in the air
.
Canister respirators must be subject to strict control.

- There should be one immediately outside the plant room; another inside, near to the points of possible leakage. There should be enough for all employees likely to be present at any one time.
- The shelf life of a properly stored respirator is about five years; once its seal is broken, however, that life is greatly reduced. So relevant dates should be on a label or log.
- They should be inspected (including hose connections and face mask seal) by a competent person every month, and by the manufacturer every six months. All this should be logged.
- Everybody who might have to use a respirator must be trained in its use. The fit should be checked.
- Respirators not on personal issue should be disinfected after use.

FIRST AID

The chief danger is gassing by chlorine fumes. Anybody affected should be sent to hospital as an emergency - because more serious symptoms may develop later.

Until a qualified doctor is available, someone who has been trained for this should administer basic first-aid measures.

A typical Material Safety Data Sheet

Sodium hypochlorite

1. Identification

NAME: Sodium Hypochlorite various strengths e.g. over 10% w/w
Synonyms: CHLOROS, HISPEC, PrimeMix Special, Everchlor, Bleacol

Emergency Phone No: 01865 407333
(24 hours)

2. Composition

Contains:

Chemical	% Conc	Symbol	Risk	Exposure	CAS	EINECS
Sodium Hypochlorite	>10% Av Cl_2	C	R31 R34		7681-52-9	231-668-3

3. Hazards

Causes burns to skin, eyes and respiratory system. Contact with acids liberates toxic gas. (Chlorine). Liberates oxygen on heating.

4. First Aid

Exposure Route	Symptom	Treatment
Inhalation:	Mists will irritate breathing passages causing coughing and wheezing	Remove from exposure, rest in fresh air and keep warm. In severe cases, or if recovery is not rapid or complete seek medical attention
Skin contact:	Irritation, blistering on prolonged contact	Drench the skin with plenty of water. Remove contaminated clothing and wash before re-use. If large areas of the skin is damaged or if irritation persists, seek medical attention
Eye contact:	Pain, redening, watering	Irrigate thoroughly with water for at least 15 minutes. Obtain medical attention
Ingestion:	Burns to upper digestive tract, stomach upset, nausea, vomiting	Wash out mouth with water. **Do not induce vomiting.** If patient is conscious, give water to drink. If patient feels unwell seek medical attention, giving attention to breathing difficulties

Immediate Treatment/Antidote: **Symptomatic treatment**

SODIUM HYPOCHLORITE

5.   Fire Fighting

Suitable extinguishers:	Use extinguisher suitable to surrounding fire conditions
Unsuitable extinguishers:	Sawdust or acidic media
Hazardous combustion products:	Oxygen and Chlorine
Special equipment for fire fighting:	A self-contained breathing apparatus and full protective clothing should be worn in fire conditions

6.   Accidental Release

Safety precautions:	Wear appropriate PPE – See section 8
Environmental precautions:	Do not allow material to contaminate drains and watercourses. Immediately inform authorities of uncontrolled discharges
Clean up procedure:	Bund or absorb material with <u>inert</u> material (e.g. sand, **NOT** sawdust). Transfer liquid if possible to salvage tank; otherwise absorb on inert material and transfer to suitable containers for waste disposal

7.   Handling & Storage

Handling

Ventilation:	Good general ventilation
Prohibited procedures & equipment:	Do not breathe mists. Do not use strong solutions on stainless steel. Do not mix with other cleaning agents

Storage

	Temperature range: cool
Keep away from:	See Section 10
Suitable storage media:	Vented containers of glass, PVC, GRP, suitably lined mild steel, high-density polyethylene.

8.   Exposure Controls/Personal Protection

Exposure limits:	None, in case of Chlorine release; 0.5ppm (1.5mg/m^3), 8 hr TWA; 1ppm (3mg/m^3), STEL
Type:	OES
Monitoring method:	As Chlorine:

Protective measures:

Respiratory:	Self-contained breathing apparatus if dealing with a major leak
Hand:	PVC or rubber gloves to BS1651
Eye:	Safety goggles to BS2092/C and/or face shield
Skin:	PVC overalls, rubber boots to BS1870
Hygiene measures:	Always wash thoroughly after handling chemicals

9. Physical & Chemical Properties

Appearance:	Clear green/yellow or pink/purple solutions
Odour:	Faint chlorinous
pH:	> 13
Boiling point/range:	110 °C
Melting point/range:	-17°C
Flammability:	Not flammable, but will liberate oxygen on heating
Oxidizing properties:	Strong oxidizing agent
Vapour pressure:	17.5mm Hg @ 20°C
Relative density:	1.26
Solubility:	Stable

10. Stability & Reactivity

Stability:	Unstable, decomposes to form Sodium Chloride and Sodium Chlorate liberating oxygen
Known hazardous reactions:	Contact with Acids liberates toxic gas (Chlorine). Violent reactions with Ammonia, Ammonium compounds and organic material
Conditions to avoid:	Heat, strong sunlight
Materials to avoid:	Acids, Ammonium salts, Methanol, Hydrocarbons, Copper, Nickel, Iron, Monel metal
Hazardous decomposition products:	Chlorine, Oxygen

11. Toxicological Information

Inhalation:	Inhalation of Chlorine gas will cause bronchial and pulmonary oedema. Symptoms may be delayed for 48 hours or more
Skin contact:	Corrosive to skin and mucous membranes
Eye contact:	Corrosive to eyes. Prolonged eye contact may result in permanent damage or blindness
Ingestion:	Ingestion may lead to formation of Chlorine gas by reaction with stomach contents. Symptoms may be delayed
LD50:	8910 mg/kg oral-rat

12. Ecological Information

Environmental effects:	
Mobility:	Soluble in water, will readily percolate through soil
Degradability:	Material will degrade slowly to Sodium Chloride, Sodium Chlorate and Oxygen
Aquatic toxicity:	Toxic to aquatic organisms. Very toxic to fish

SODIUM HYPOCHLORITE

13. Disposal

Substance: Via an authorised waste disposal contractor to an approved waste disposal site, observing all local and national legislation

Container: As substance. Used containers must not be cut up or punctured until completely purged of product residues

14. Transport Information

SIN/UN number: 1791   ADR Class/Item No. 8 - 61°(c)
Primary Hazard: Corrosive
Packing Group: III   Subsidiary hazard
H.I number: 80   UK Emergency action code 2x

15. Regulatory Information

Supply label details   Ref CHIP 97

Label name: Sodium Hypochlorite Solution .... % Av Cl_2
Symbols: Corrosive
Risk phrases: R31   Contact with Acid liberates toxic gas
     R34   Causes burns
Safety phrases: S1/2   Keep locked up and out of reach of children
     S28   After contact with skin, wash immediately with plenty of water
     S45   In case of accident or if you feel unwell, seek medical advice immediately (show label where possible)
     S50   Do not mix with Acidic materials
E E C No.   231-668-3

16. Other Information

This material is usually used for: Water treatment, cleaning, disinfecting, bleaching
This data sheet was prepared in accordance with directive 91/155/EEC

The information contained in this data sheet does not constitute an assessment of workplace risks.

All chemicals may present unforeseen risks and should be used with caution. We cannot guarantee the risks referred to above are the only risks present. The final choice of the application of a product is the sole responsibility of the user.

This information is provided as a guide to the use of the product and is correct to the best of our knowledge. However, neither (the manufacturer) nor PWTAG can offer any guarantee as to its accuracy or exhaustiveness.

Legal Disclaimer:

The above information is based on the present state of knowledge of the product at the time of publication. It is given in good faith, no warranty is implied with respect to the quality or the specification of the product. The user must satisfy himself that the product is entirely suitable for his purpose.

Revision No: June 1998 (Replaces MSDS Jan 1998)

Problem sorter

Problem	Possible reasons	Action	Page
pH too high	Mains water is alkaline (and hard)	Add more acid	79
	Alkaline disinfectant used	Consider changing to acid disinfectant Adjust regularly/frequently/automatically by acid dosing	31 79
pH too low	Mains water is acidic	Add more alkali	77
	Acidic disinfectant used	Consider changing to alkaline disinfectant Adjust regularly/frequently/automatically by alkali dosing	31 77
pH erratic	Water is not buffered - alkalinity too low	Check and raise alkalinity	79
	Dosing erratic	Check dosing accuracy and frequency	51
pH difficult to change	Water too buffered - alkalinity too high	Check and lower alkalinity	79
Cloudy, dirty water	Bathing load too high	Reduce bathing load	19
	Filtration inadequate	Check filter, flow rate, backwash	71, 73
Cloudy, clean water	Hardness salts coming out of solution	Check and where necessary correct pH, alkalinity, hardness	77-80
	Entrained air or coagulant	Check on coagulant dosing. Check air release on filters; air leaks on suction side of pump	75, 123
Cloudy, coloured water (outdoor pools mainly)	Algae - sunlight, poor hydraulics	Increase residual level, backwash	103
Slimy, coloured growth on pool walls, floor, black on grouting	Algae - sunlight, poor hydraulics	Without bathers, brush or vacuum off algae, increase residual level, backwash	103
Water has bad taste or smell - irritates eyes and throat	High combined chlorine	Check combined chlorine levels and type; be prepared to dilute or correct free chlorine level	81-83
	pH wrong	Check and correct if necessary	77

Problem	Possible reasons	Action	Page
Chlorine level difficult to maintain	Sunlight	Consider a stabiliser (cyanuric acid)	42
	Bather pollution	Reduce bathing load	19
	Filter blocked, turnover reduced, hydraulics poor	Check filter, strainer, flow rate, and valves	75, 123
Filter blocked (pressure across it too high)	Too infrequent backwashing/ cleaning - or scale	Check and improve backwash effectiveness; consider replacing sand	73, 75
	Incorrect coagulant dosing	Check coagulant dosing; inspect filter	75, 123
Water clarity generally poor	Wrong filter or incorrect use	Check filtration type and rate, sand condition, procedures (backwashing etc)	71, 73, 75
	Insufficient chlorine	Check and correct free chlorine residual	81-83
	Incorrect or no coagulant	Check coagulant use	75
Hard scale on surfaces, fittings, pipes etc; water may feel harsh	Hardness salts coming out of solution	Check and where necessary correct pH, alkalinity, hardness	77-80
Cannot get test kit readings for free chlorine residual	Chlorine levels too high	Test a 50:50 diluted water sample	83
	Chlorine levels too low	Check chlorine dosing	51
Poor air quality	Air circulation poor	Check air handling - introduce more fresh air	116
	Combined chlorine too high	Restore recommended chlorine levels	83
	Temperature too high	Reduce to recommended levels	116
Water has salty tasty	Dissolved solids to high	Dilute	11
Staining at water inlet	Iron salts coming out of solution	Check pH, water balance, coagulation	77, 80, 75
Dull water, no sparkle	Could be anything	Check everything - disinfection, water balance, filtration, coagulation, etc	9-143

Organisations

Pool Water Treatment Advisory Group

PWTAG was inaugurated in December 1984, the year that the Department of the Environment Sub-Committee on the Treatment of Water in Swimming Pools was wound up. Like that DoE sub-committee, the independent PWTAG has a membership drawn from a wide range of relevant statutory, voluntary and professional bodies.

PWTAG has a major role in the treatment and quality of swimming pool water, through:

- monitoring and advising on important issues and developments
- research projects
- publishing reports, guidance and press releases
- reviewing existing advice and publications.

This work covers water in all swimming and leisure pools used by the public, whether under public or private ownership and management. Only domestic pools are excluded. It is involved in research at Cranfield University (see below) and elsewhere; work on guidelines and standards; product assessment; advice to pool managers and operators, local authorities, industry, etc; and the investigation of incidents. Some of the issues addressed by PWTAG arise from within the group; many come from outside - either as specific suggestions, or as a consequence of PWTAG's advisory role.

In general, PWTAG acts as a ginger group, a focus for debate and improvement in management and operational standards.

Membership
Eleven organisations make up the membership of PWTAG. Technical advisers have also been appointed to provide specialist help.

Current members
Sport England (David Butler)
Dept for Education & Employment (Richard Daniels)
Ministry of Defence (Stuart Wainwright)
Amateur Swimming Association (Noel Winter)
British Association for Chemical Specialities
(Mike Parry)
British Water (Andy Elphick)

Chartered Institute of Environmental Health
(Terry Price)
Institute of Sport & Recreation Management
(Ralph Riley)
Institute of Leisure & Amenity Management
(Janice Calvert)
Institute of Engineers of Ireland (Tom Devin)
Swimming Pool & Allied Trades Association
(Howard Gosling)

Technical advisers
Chartered Institution of Building Services Engineers
(Dave Bosher)
Dept of the Environment, Transport & the Regions
(Owen Hydes)
Dept of Health (Rob Griffin)
Public Health Laboratory Service (Dr Gordon Nichols)
Dr Phil Penny
Dave Whittingham

The part-time Secretary, Brian Guthrie, is the only paid officer.

Finance
PWTAG's income comes largely from Sport England and other membership subscriptions. There is also income from the sale of books. PWTAG has always, in principle, welcomed sponsorship to help fund its research objectives. Income from all sources has been directed particularly towards the Pool Water Research Foundation.

Pool Water Research Foundation
In 1994 PWTAG established the Pool Water Research Foundation (PWRF) at Cranfield University. The intention has been to combine the scientific rigour of academic research with realistic, pool-based investigation. Research is based largely on a one-seventh-scale swimming pool rig, its design and operation based on a real 25m pool. Its filtration, water treatment, etc are appropriately scaled.

The Science & Engineering Research Council funded a Total Technology PhD studentship at PWRF. A number of other, short-term investigations were mounted through MSc studentships. The Pool Water Treatment Advisory Group, as industrial sponsor, helped support the students financially, and was responsible for capital and running costs. Funding was from PWTAG's membership subscription income, from the sale of books, and from the support of industrial and other sponsors.

The research so far has focused on factors affecting the production of trihalomethanes and other disinfection byproducts. As expected, chloroform was the main THM produced under chlorination, and bromoform the chief product of bromination. Bromoform levels during bromination were about three times higher than chloroform levels during chlorination. The levels of THM produced increased by about 50% when pollution loading levels were stepped up. Increasing disinfectant concentrations did not have such a marked effect. But more significant, perhaps, was the discovery that a rapid increase in disinfectant concentration produced a rapid increase in THMs - as much as 200% up in some cases. And the same was true when pollution loading levels were added intermittently, rather than continuously.

This underlines the importance of establishing, as far as possible, a steady bathing load in swimming pools; also the value of smooth control of disinfectant dosing, rather than a pattern of non-systematic disinfection with occasional 'shock' dosing. (Results from monitoring chloramines reinforced this message.)

Research has also included a survey of pool operators's attitudes to their choice of disinfection and investigations of the effects of ozone, carbon filtration and ultraviolet irradiation. The work continues. For details of research findings, contact PWTAG's secretary (details below).

Contact
The Pool Water Treatment Advisory Group's hope is that the Pool Water Research Foundation will increasingly act as a focus for research on pool water issues, and a broker for further work done at Cranfield. Inquiries about PWRF or PWTAG to Brian Guthrie
Field House, Thrandeston, Diss, Norfolk IP21 4BU
Phone 01379 783678, fax 01379 783865
Email guthrie@pwtag.demon.co.uk).

Other organisations

Amateur Swimming Association
Harold Fern House, Derby Square, Loughborough, Leicestershire LE11 0AL (01509 230431)

British Water
1 Queen Anne's Gate, London SW1H 9BT
(0171 957 4554)

Chartered Institute of Environmental Health
Chadwick Court, 15 Hatfields, London SE1 8DJ
(0171 928 6006)

Chartered Institution of Building Services Engineers
Delta House, 222 Balham High Road,
London SW12 9BS (0181 675 5211)

Institute of Leisure & Amenity Management
ILAM House, Lower Basildon, Reading, Berkshire
RG8 9NE (01491 874800)

Institute of Sport and Recreation Management
Giffard House, 36-38 Sherrard Street, Melton Mowbray, Leicestershire LE13 1XJ (01664 565531)

Institute of Swimming Pool Engineers Limited
PO Box 3089, Halstead, Essex CO9 4SB
(01440 785999)

Public Health Laboratory Service
HQ, 61 Colindale Avenue, London NW9 5DF
(0181 200 1295)

Sport England
16 Upper Woburn Place, London WC1H 0QP
(0171 273 1500)

Swimming Pool and Allied Trades Association
SPATA House, Junction Road, Andover,
Hampshire SP10 3QT (01264 356210)

Bibliography

Code of Practice for ozone plant for swimming pool water treatment. British Water/Pool Water Treatment Advisory Group 1990. £10 from British Water, 1 Queen Anne's Gate, London SW1H 9BT (0171 957 4554)

Guidance Note - Swimming Pools: Design. Sport England from Sport England Publications (0990 210255)

Handbook of Sports and Recreational Building Design Vol 3 Swimming pools and ice rinks. Butterworth 1999, ISBN 0750622563. £80 from Sport England Publications (0990 210255)

Health Building Note 8 (includes information on hydrotherapy pools) NHS Estates. From HMSO, PO Box 276, London SW8 5DT (0171 873 9090)

Hygiene for Hydrotherapy Pools. Public Health Laboratory Service 2nd edition in preparation. PHLS Publications, 61 Colindale Avenue, London NW9 5DF

Hygiene for Spa Pools. Public Health Laboratory Service 1994, ISBN 0901144371. £6.50 from PHLS Publications, 61 Colindale Avenue, London NW9 5DF

Institute of Sport & Recreation Management (ISRM) publications include 36 information notes mainly on pool safety issues and publications on plant rooms, diving and pool plant operation, etc. ISRM, Giffard House, 36-38 Sherrard Street, Melton Mowbray, Leicestershire LE13 1XJ (01664 565531)

List of substances and products approved for use in the production of potable water from seawater or brackish water and for the treatment of swimming pool water. Committee on Chemicals and Materials of Construction for use in Public Water Supply and Swimming Pools, DETR Drinking Water Inspectorate, Ashdown House, 2/E5, 123 Victoria Street, London SW1P 3PY (0171 890 5996). Website www.dwi.detr.gov.uk/list/index.htm The List is published in *Recreation*, the monthly magazine of the ISRM

Managing Health and Safety in Swimming Pools. Health & Safety Commission and Sport England 1999, ISBN 0717613887. £10 from Sport England

Publications (phone 0990 210255) and HSE Books (01787 881165)

Managing school facilities Guide 2 Swimming pools. Department for Education & Employment. From HMSO, PO Box 276, London SW8 5DT (0171 873 9090)

The prevention or control of legionellosis (including Legionnaires' disease). Approved Code of Practice L8 HSE Books 1995, ISBN 0717607321. From HSE Books (01787 881165)

Report 71 - The Microbiology of Water 1994: Part 1 - Drinking Water. ISBN 0117530107 £25 from HMSO, PO Box 276, London SW8 5DT (0171 873 9090)

Swimming Pool and Allied Trades Association (SPATA) publications include *Standards for Residential and Semi-public Swimming pools,* three volumes - £10 each; and *Standards for Spa Pools Installation, Chemical & Water treatment* - £10. From SPATA House, Junction Road, Andover, Hampshire SP10 3QT (01264 356210)

Stainless steel in swimming pool buildings: A guide to selection and use. Nickel Development Institute 1995, Publication no 12 010. Free from NiDI (01527 584777)

World Health Organisation Guidelines for Drinking Water Volume 1 Recommendations ISBN 9241544600 (£25) , Volume 2 Health criteria ISBN 941544805 (£125). From HMSO, PO Box 276, London SW8 5DT (0171 873 9090)

Hydrotherapy pools of the future - the avoidance of health problems. PT Penny. *Journal of Hospital Infection,* 1991 Volume 18, Supplement A, pp 535-542

Swimming Pool Dermatoses associated with the use of Bromine Disinfectant. PT Penny, RJG Rycroft. *British Medical Journal* 13 August 1983

The Building Research Establishment Energy Conservation Support Group produces a number of guides relevant to swimming pool design and management. From BRECSU, Garston, Watford WD2 7JR (01923 894040)

Index/Glossary

Halogen
   The chemical family that includes chlorine and bromine (and iodine)
Halamines 94
   The products of the reaction between halogen disinfectants and ammonia from urea in sweat and urine
Hardness 79
   A measure of all the calcium and magnesium salts in pool water (total hardness); see also calcium, permanent and temporary hardness
Health effects of byproducts 94
Health & Safety at Work, Etc Act 1974 119, 122
Health & Safety Executive 119
Healthy swimming 87
Heat exchanger - see calorifier
Heating 115
Hepatitis 87, 88, 90
   Viral blood diseases - A and B
HIV 20, 87, 91
   Human immunodeficiency virus
Holidaymaker's rash 91
Humic acid 10, 75, 94
   A constituent of water that reacts with halogen disinfectants to form trihalomethanes
Humidity 116
   A measure of the moisture in the atmosphere
Hydraulics 22, 26, 63
   The science of fluid mechanics - applied here to circulation
Hydrochloric acid HCl 53, 78
   An acid used (with care) to lower pool water pH value
Hydrogen peroxide 83
Hydrotherapy pools 15
Hypobromous acid 42, 43
   The main active factor in all bromine disinfectants
Hypochlorous acid 37, 82
   The main active factor in all chlorine disinfectants
Hypochlorite - electrolytic generation 40

I

Incubation 97, 100
   Leaving pool water samples at a steady temperature on a nutrient medium to grow any microorganisms present
Infections 87
Inflammation 90
   Redness and swelling

Inlets 22, 67
   The ducts that carry water into the pool basin
Ions 44
   Electrically charged chemical particles
Iron chloride 75
Iron sulphate 75

J

Jacuzzi 18
   A brand of whirlpool spa

L

Langelier index 80
   One measure of balanced water
Learner pools 15
Lecithin (Azolectin) 99
   A neutraliser used (with Tween 80) for microbiological testing of water disinfected with polymeric biguanides
Legionnaires' disease 87, 92
   A serious respiratory illness caused by *Legionella pneumophila* in water sprays
Legislation 31, 102, 119, 122
Leptospira 87
Leisure pools 15, 21, 64
Lifeguards 118
Log sheet 121

M

Magnetism 44
Mains water 9
Maintenance 123
Managers 118
Managing health & safety in swimming pools 119, 138
Material safety data sheets (MSDSs) 102, 129
Membrane filtration method 98
   Used in monitoring coliforms
Meningitis 87, 92
Methaemoglobinaemia 95
   A blood condition caused by, among other things, chlorites
Microflocculation 45
   Monitoring chlorine disinfection
Monochloramine 38, 82, 94
Moveable floors 14, 21, 67, 127
Mucus 28
Multi-grade filters 72
Multiple tube method 98
   Used in monitoring coliforms
Mycobacterium 88

N

Naegleria fowleri 88, 92
   An amoeba which can cause meningitis
Nappies 30, 93
Nasopharyngeal infection 90
   Infection in the nose/throat region
New pool rash 91
Nitrogen trichloride 39, 83
   The most irritant of the chloramines
Nutrient medium 97, 98
   A substance that will grow bacteria

O

Operation 24, 120
Organic 39, 41, 82
   A confusing term, as it is used to describe chemicals based on carbon, substances of human origin eg sweat, and untreated food.
Organisations 136
Otitis externa and media 92
Outdoor pools 16, 42
Outlets 22, 65
   The ducts that carry water from the pool basin
Overflow channels 65
Oxidation 37
   In pool water chemistry, the process by which disinfectants destroy pollution
Ozone 10, 34, 45
Ozone Plant Code of Practice 43, 138

P

PAC - see Polyaluminium chloride
Paddling pools 16
Pathogens 88
   Disease-causing microorganisms
Permanent hardness 79
   That part which does not precipitate from the water on heating; it consists of calcium and magnesium salts other than carbonates and bicarbonates
pH 32, 37, 77
Pharyngo-conjunctival fever 90
Phosphates 10, 103
Plantar warts - see Verrucas
Plant room 23, 26, 112
Plate count - see Colony count
Plunge pools 17
Polio 87
Pollution from bathers 28
Polyaluminium chloride (PAC) 75, 109

V

Ventilation 116
Verrucas (plantar warts) 29, 88, 90
   A foot infection
Viruses 90
   Submicroscopic infective agents
Vomit 91

W

Water balance - see Balanced water
Water standards 9
Water treatment 25
Waterslide splashdown pools 18, 21
Wave pools 18
Whirlpool spas 18
Whirlpool folliculitis - see Folliculitis
World Health Organisation (WHO) 4, 94

Z

Zeolite 44